CW00376842

Bibliometrics: Use and Abuse in the Review of Research Performance

Other titles in the Wenner-Gren International Series
published by Portland Press:

Trust in Universities
edited by L. Engwall and P. Scott
2013 ISBN 978 1 85578 194 8

From Information to Knowledge;
from Knowledge to Wisdom
edited by E. De Corte and J.E. Fenstad
2010 ISBN 978 1 85578 171 1

The University in the Market
edited by L. Engwall and D. Weaire
2008 ISBN 978 1 85578 168 9

The Formative Years of Scholars
edited by U. Teichler
2006 ISBN 978 1 85578 164 1

Excellence in Higher Education
edited by E. De Corte
2003 ISBN 978 1 85578 152 8

Prostasomes
edited by G. Ronquist and B.O. Nilsson
2002 ISBN 978 1 85578 151 1

Symmetry 2000
edited by I. Hargittai and T.C. Laurent
2002 ISBN 978 1 85578 149 8

Virtual University? Educational Environments
of the Future
edited by H.J. van der Molen
2001 ISBN 978 1 85578 145 0

Advances in Strabismus Research:
Basic and Clinical Aspects
edited by G. Lennerstrand and J. Ygge
2000 ISBN 978 1 85578 144 3

Lifelong Learning Policy and Research
edited by A. Tuijnman and T. Schuller
1999 ISBN 978 1 85578 134 4

The Impact of Electronic Publishing
on the Academic Community
edited by I. Butterworth
1998 ISBN 978 1 85578 122 1

WENNER-GREN INTERNATIONAL SERIES

VOLUME 87

Bibliometrics: Use and Abuse in the Review of Research Performance

Proceedings from a symposium held
in Stockholm, 23–25 May 2013

Edited by

Wim Blockmans
Lars Engwall
Denis Weaire

Published by Portland Press Limited, Third Floor, Charles Darwin House,
12 Roger Street, London WC1N 2JU, U.K.
Tel: +44 (0)20 7685 2410; e-mail: editorial@portlandpress.com
www.portlandpress.com

ISBN 978-1-85578-195-5

British Library Cataloguing in Publication Data
A catalogue record for this book is available from the British Library

Originated by The Manila Typesetting Company, The Philippines
Printed in Great Britain by Henry Ling Limited, Dorchester

Contents

This book is based on the presentations and discussions at a symposium jointly arranged by Academia Europaea (www.ae-info.org) and the Wenner-Gren Foundations held in Stockholm in late May 2013. The conference was part of the HERCULES (Higher Education, Research and Culture in European Society) initiative within Academia Europaea. The programme was planned by an Organizing Committee consisting of Professors Wim Blockmans, Leiden, The Netherlands (chair); Eric De Corte, Leuven, Belgium; Lars Engwall, Uppsala, Sweden; Jan Reedijk, Leiden, The Netherlands; and Denis Weaire, Dublin, Ireland.

The symposium and the present volume have been generously supported financially by the Wenner-Gren Foundations, for which we are very grateful. We also like to thank the Foundations for their administrative support. Our special thanks go to Professor Bertil Daneholt, former Science Secretary of the Foundations, the present Scientific Secretary Professor Britt-Marie Sjöberg and the Administrative Assistant, Maria Helgöstam. We also thank our colleagues in the Organizing Committee as well as the Executive Secretary of the Academia Europaea, David Coates and his Administrative Assistant, Teresa McGovern for their assistance in the preparation of the Symposium.

Wim Blockmans
Lars Engwall
Denis Weaire

Giovanni Abramo
Laboratory for studies of Research and Technology Transfer at the Institute for System Analysis and Computer Science (IASI-CNR), University of Tor Vergata, Roma
giovanni.abramo@uniroma2.it

Wim Blockmans
Emeritus Professor in History at Leiden University, and former Rector of The Netherlands Institute for Advanced Study in the Humanities and Social Sciences
wimblockmans7@gmail.com

Stéphanie Chatelain-Ponroy
Conservatoire National des Arts et Métiers, Paris
stephanie.chatelain@cnam.fr

Ciriaco Andrea D'Angelo
Department of Engineering and Management, University of Rome 'Tor Vergata'
dangelo@dii.uniroma2.it

Tim Engels
Department of Research Affairs and Centre for Research and Development Monitoring, University of Antwerp
tim.engels@uantwerpen.be

Lars Engwall
Emeritus Professor of Management at Uppsala University
lars.engwall@fek.uu.se

Michel Gevers
Emeritus Professor in Mathematical Engineering, ICTEAM, at Université catholique de Louvain, Louvain la Neuve
michel.gevers@uclouvain.be

Pol Ghesquière
Professor in Learning Disabilities and Special Education, and Research Coordinator Social Sciences and Humanities at the Catholic University Leuven. He is President of the Panel for the Construction of the Flemish Academic Bibliographic Database for SS&H
pol.ghesquiere@ppw.kuleuven.be

Jane Grimson
Professor of Health Informatics, School of Computer Science and Statistics, Trinity College, Dublin
jane.grimson@tcd.ie

Nicola Gulley
Editorial Director of IOP Publishing, Bristol
nicola.gulley@iop.org

Giuseppe Longo
Research Director in Informatics and Epistemology, Centre Cavaillès, République des
Savoirs, CNRS and Collège de France et École Normale Supérieure, Paris
giuseppe.longo@ens.fr

Stéphanie Mignot-Gérard
Université Paris-Est, Créteil
stephanie.mignot-gerard@u-pec.fr

Christine Musselin
Professor in Sociology and Scientific Director of Sciences Po, Paris
christine.musselin@sciencespo.fr

Anthony F.J. van Raan
Professor Science Studies at Leiden University and former Director of CWTS
vanraan@cwts.leidenuniv.nl

Jan Reedijk
Professor and former Scientific Director of the Leiden Institute of Chemistry,
Leiden University
reedijk@chem.leidenuniv.nl

Samuel Sponem
HEC Montreal
samuel.sponem@hec.ca

Frederik Verleysen
Centre for Research and Development Monitoring, University of Antwerp
frederik.verleysen@uantwerpen.be

Denis Weaire
Emeritus Professor of Physics, Trinity College, Dublin
dweaire@tcd.ie

Linda Wedlin
Associate Professor and Lecturer at the Department of Business Studies,
Uppsala University
linda.wedlin@fek.uu.se

Milena Žic Fuchs
Professor in English Linguistics at the University of Zagreb and former
Chair of the Standing Committee for the Humanities of the European Science
Foundation
mzicfuch@ffzg.hr

AERES	Agence d´Evaluation de la Recherche et de l´Enseignement Supérieur/Evaluation Agency for Research and Higher Education
ANR	Agence Nationale de la Recherche/The French National Research Agency
ARC	Australian Research Council
ARWU	Academic Ranking of World Universities
BC	bibliographic coupling
BOF	Bijzonder Onderzoeksfonds/University Research Fund
CC	co-citation
CNÉ	Conseil national de l´évaluation des universités/National Council for the Evaluation of Universities
CNRS	Centre National de la Recherche Scientifique/National Centre for Scientific Research
COUNTER	Counting Online Usage of Networked Electronic Resources
CRIStin	Current Research Information System in Norway
CWTS	Centre for Science and Technology Studies
DMU	Decision Making Unit
DOI	digital object identifier
DORA	Declaration on Research Assessment
ECOOM	Expertisecentrum Onderzoek en Ontwikkelingsmonitoring/Centre for Research and Development Monitoring
ERC	European Research Council
ERIH	European Reference Index for the Humanities
ESF	European Science Foundation
FP7	Seventh Framework Programme
FSS	Fractional Scientific Strength
GP	Gezaghebbend Panel/Authoritative Panel
GPRC	Guaranteed Peer Reviewed Content
HERD	Higher Education Research and Development
h-index	Hirsch-index
HSMR	Hospital Standardised Mortality Ratio
HSS	humanities and social sciences
IF	impact factor
INRA	Institut National de la Recherche Agronomique/French National Institute for Agricultural Research
INSERM	Institut National de la Santé et de la Recherche Médicale/French Institute of Health and Medical Research
IREG	International Ranking Expert Group
JCR	Journal Citation Reports
JIF	journal impact factor
JWARP	Journal of Water Resource and Protection
KPI	Key Performance Indicators
LOPRI	Loi d'Orientation pour la Recherche et l'Innovation/Act for Research and Innovation
LSE	London School of Economics
LUMC	Leiden University Medical Centre
M&E	Monitoring and Evaluation
MCS	mean citation score

MMR	measles, mumps and rubella
MNCS	mean normalized citation score
NI	Normalized Impact
NS	natural sciences
OA	open access
OECD	Organisation for Economic Cooperation and Development
PRFS	performance based research funding system
QS	Quacquarelli Symonds
RAE	Research Assessment Exercise
ROARS	Return On Academic ReSearch
SCI	Science Citation Index
SDS	Scientific Disciplinary Sector
SJTU	Shanghai Jiao Tong University
SLR	Sauvons la recherche/Save Research
SLU	Sauvons l'université/Save the University
SNIP	source normalized impact per paper
STM	science, technology and medicine
THES	Times Higher Education Supplement
TRIF	Thomson Reuters Impact Factor
UDA	University Disciplinary Area
VABB-SHW	Vlaams Academisch Bibliografisch Bestand voor de Sociale en Humane Wetenschappen/Flemish Academic Bibliographic Database for the Social Sciences and Humanities
VUV	Flemish Publishers' Association
WoS	Web of Science

PART I: BASIC CONSIDERATIONS

Bibliometrics: issues and context

Lars Engwall*[1], Wim Blockmans†[2] and Denis Weaire‡[3]
*Department of Business Studies, Uppsala University, Sweden, †Institute for History, Leiden University, The Netherlands, and ‡Institute of Physics, Trinity College Dublin, The University of Dublin, Ireland

Introduction

Academic institutions have two basic missions: first, to disseminate knowledge (primarily education, but also popularization), and secondly, to create new knowledge (research). Both of these missions include another significant task: quality assessment. In terms of the first mission, academic teachers examine and grade students for their understanding of course material, thereby screening candidates for the labour market [1]. These assessments normally take place inside institutions, although today we can see increasing efforts from authorities to undertake external reviews of standards [2]. Since research is international, such external examinations have long been the case for this second mission. A basic principle for these assessments is the peer-review system, i.e. that the quality of academic work is examined by colleagues in a particular scientific field. This is true for hiring and promotion decisions, assessments of journal manuscripts and research proposals as well as evaluations of institutions.

During the last couple of decades, bibliometrics has come to play a more and more significant role in the peer-review system [3]. This is a result of (i) the development of modern information technology, (ii) a strong expansion of the number of researchers, and (iii) the growth in the number of publication outlets [4]. As a result, bibliometrics has increasingly become the yardstick for quality, a development that has attracted criticism among researchers. In the words of the 1991 Chemistry Nobel Laureate, Richard R. Ernst [5]:

> *"We are deeply convinced that human ingenuity and creativity are beyond all conceivable quantitative measure. [...] The present hype of bibliometry made it plainly obvious that judging the quality of science publications and science projects by bibliometric measures alone is inadequate. [...] Start reading papers instead of merely rating them by counting citations!"*

When a Nobel Prize Laureate uses such strong language, the scientific community and science policymakers should pay attention. Although private companies, publishing houses, consultancies and the boards of scientific institutions are organizing perpetuum mobiles of evaluations, the scientific community grows increasingly impatient with the heavy burden imposed by this elaborate evaluation carousel. Whereas the investment in working time and money is evident, the effects are all but transparent and the methodological controversies are far from solved.

[1]Email: lars.engwall@fek.uu.se
[2]Email: wimblockmans7@gmail.com
[3]Email: dweaire@tcd.ie

The main objection is surely the reduction in evaluation to sheer metrics, as a proxy for the desire for a standardized evaluation of a great variety of achievements.

Measuring versus quality

In biosciences and most of the natural sciences, bibliometrics is a well-established practice, widely accepted as a tool in the adjudication of access to scarce resources, on a personal and an institutional level. It is claimed that systemic errors and fallacies such as self-quotation, mutual referencing and negative references may be filtered out, especially in domains with high numbers of researchers. Standardized publication cultures in international journals and a global scientific forum reinforce the applicability of citation indices. They can be used for the ranking of journals, as well as for that of research groups and individual researchers. Collective authorship, however, raises the question of each individual's role, as practices in this respect differ between disciplines.

However, there are several fundamental concerns about the prevailing review systems:

1. To what extent are the current peer-review systems favouring fashionable and standard research, or able to recognize truly groundbreaking ideas? Is there a tension between inherently qualitative characteristics, such as originality and creativity and quantification?
2. Are the current bibliometric systems generally applicable? Engineering, mathematics, computer sciences, as well as most of the social sciences and humanities work with distinctive publication cultures appropriate to their societal mission, forum and target groups. This implies a far greater variety of publication formats in patents, websites, reports, national journals, books and the use of a great number of national languages. In these disciplines, Anglophone researchers may even be uninformed about a considerable body of knowledge published in other languages.
3. Do the self-interested actions of ambitious authors, profit-seeking publishing houses, specialized research bureaus and science administrators lead to systemic distortions of bibliometric measures?
4. Given the amount of the publications under review, and the scope of evaluation committees on an institutional level, are reviewers materially able to assess the quality of research?
5. Is the evaluation work hampering scientific progress by taking time away from research? It is an often-heard argument that in the life of scholars today too much time is taken up by evaluating others and being evaluated by others.

Bibliometrics in context

It is appropriate to put bibliometrics into a wider context. In so doing, we can use a more general model of the governance of academic institutions [6]. It implies, as shown in Figure 1, that organizations are under governance from three types of actors: authorities, market actors and scrutinizers.

Academic institutions have traditionally been characterized by autonomy, i.e. self-governance. There are, in principle, no barriers to starting up academic institutions, but in order to acquire trust they need recognition from authorities (Figure 1, left-hand side). For the medieval universities, this was achieved through bulls from the Pope, and later on, sovereigns provided their recognition [7–9]. This in turn implied certain external rules for the academic institutions, and with the passage of time these have become more forceful as governments have increasingly provided their financial means. More and more, they have been subject to market forces (Figure 1, right-hand side) through various kinds of market information (careers of alumni, publication achievements, successes in grant applications, etc.). These market forces have increased as governments have outsourced their authority to the market to an increasing extent by moving from university block grants to financing through project grants [2]. At the same time, we can also see an increasing role for scrutinizers, i.e. the media, NGOs, auditing bodies and so on (Figure 1, bottom). They provide norms for how the organizations should behave. So, even if academic institutions are characterized by a relatively high degree of autonomy, they are influenced by rules, market information and norms [10].

Although there are a lot of complaints in academia regarding biblio- metrics, it was not invented by the authorities. Rather, it is an outcome of an interaction between academia and market actors. There can be no doubt that the present market for publishing is grounded in the desire of scholars to have their results published. This in turn has resulted in the foundation of a large number of journals, often in the form of publications of professional associations. And, these journals have been attractive to publishing houses, since they provide two advantages. First, they are subsidized by the academic community through their willingness to submit and review manuscripts without any remuneration. Secondly, they provide contacts with prospective authors of textbooks, as well as

Figure 1

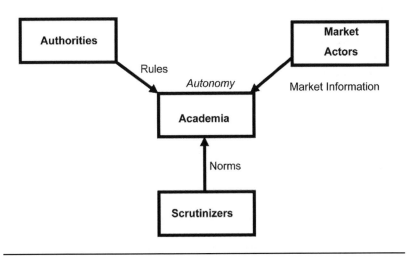

Academia, authorities, market actors and scrutinizers

with significant gatekeepers in the selection of course literature. No wonder the number of journals is increasing through this symbiosis between academia and market actors! Amidst the resulting plethora of publications and the journals that feed on them, how is one to distil some estimates of quality? Citation analysis, originally designed to assist the research process itself, has stepped into this role.

At the same time it should be noted that, although there are a number of complaints regarding bibliometrics (cf. above), academia itself is not an innocent victim thereof. Instead, citation figures and impact factors are often used by institutions as well as individuals in order to enhance reputations and in order to get access to more resources. So it has even become more and more common to use bibliometrics in the assessment of scholars instead of reading the publications they offer for evaluation. This means an outsourcing to other actors (editors and reviewers) of one of the most important tasks of academia.

The grip of bibliometrics on academia has been reinforced by reactions of the two other types of actors in Figure 1: scrutinizers and authorities. For the scrutinizers, ranking systems constitute a particularly important feature, and such systems pay considerable attention to bibliometrics [11]. Similarly, over the course of time, authorities have shown an increasing interest in bibliometrics as a quality indicator. So, bibliometrics has become a significant part of the governance system outlined in Figure 1.

Bibliometrics under scrutiny

Out of the above critique the following questions arise:

- Do researchers today face an overload of evaluation activities of all kinds on both sides of the process, including journal article and other manuscript reviews?
- Does this time pressure tend to jeopardize the quality of assessments?
- How serious is the bias favouring the English-speaking world?
- Are the humanities and the social sciences, which do not fit well in to the system, seriously mistreated?
- How are we to balance the costs of the evaluation system, the advancement of science and its attendant economic benefits, and the profits made by private companies?

Guided by this critique, the Academia Europaea and the Wenner-Gren Foundations found it appropriate to jointly organize a symposium on the culture of accountability, and the techniques to establish indicators of quality on various levels, from the individual research paper to whole universities. It took place on 23–25 May 2013 in Stockholm, Sweden, and attracted some 60 participants, among them a dozen speakers presenting papers on various aspects of bibliometrics. The present volume contains the revised versions of these papers.

The volume consists of five parts and a conclusion. The first, in addition to this introductory chapter, includes a contribution by Giuseppe Longo, École Normale Supérieure, who delves deep into the philosophy of science, which he contrasts with democratic mechanisms. He stresses the significance of minority thinking for both democracy and scientific development, which is at odds with 'democratic' and 'normalizing' thinking as reflected by bibliometrics. He thereby points to the need for editors to find open-minded referees in order to pave the way for original ideas. The next four parts deal with:

- Instruments of measurement
- Indicators for rankings
- Journals, editors and publishers
- Bibliometrics in the humanities and the social sciences

The second part contains two contributions on the techniques for measuring citations and impact. In the first one, Ton (A.F.J.) van Raan, the founding father of CWTS (Centre for Science and Technology Studies) at Leiden University, provides an overview of the application of bibliometrics at different levels of aggregation and in different contexts. He presents a new 'crown indicator' and acknowledges 11 issues on which statistical methods should still be refined to avoid pitfalls and sources of error. In addition, he discusses the creation and use of science maps based on word or citation similarity of publications. In an appendix, he provides an overview of the current bibliometric indicators. Further perspectives are provided by Jane Grimson, Trinity College Dublin, who draws parallels between biblio-metrics and indicators used in the field of healthcare. In so doing, she discusses the lessons to be learnt from the healthcare sector in assessing research quality. In addition to the current arguments, she demonstrates that "existing approaches to the measurement of research quality are largely gender blind".

In the third part, the volume turns to methodological critics on the current use of indicators, especially for rankings of universities on a global scale. Michel Gevers, Université catholique de Louvain, presents an analysis of scientific impact versus investments. After a critical appraisal of scientific performance indicators, he compares the performances of a range of countries in an analysis where citation numbers are normalized with respect to the budget invested by that country in scientific research at higher-education institutions. Giovanni Abramo (National Research Council of Italy) and Ciriaco Andrea D'Angelo (University of Rome 'Tor Vergata') choose the productivity of the investments in research as their focus. They make a critical assessment of the widely used h-index (Hirsch-index) by applying this measure to evaluate the performance of Italian universities. The authors insist on the necessity to normalize performance indicators by the productivity of individuals, groups or institutions, as well as by the characteristics of any field's publication styles. Adding up or averaging different datasets leads to distortions and are scientifically incorrect. This analysis leads Abramo and D'Angelo to the conclusion that research evaluations based on the h-index are of little value or may even be dangerous for decision-makers. They are followed by Linda Wedlin of Uppsala University, who discusses how global comparisons matter. She points out how rankings have created an image of a global higher education field, which has not always had positive effects. A counterforce, according to Linda Wedlin, is that the picture is becoming diverse as a result of a multitude of rankings. At the same time she concludes that changes in the system are slow.

Part four discusses the problems of publishers of journals, and their editors. Nicola Gulley, of IOP Publishing, stresses that all parties involved in the process are accountable for results, but she warns against misinterpretation of any single metric taken out of context. Techniques are quickly evolving, such as the download counting of articles, which can be manipulated in the social media. The central question is whether popularity indicates quality. In a subsequent chapter, Jan Reedijk, Leiden University, discusses the value and accuracy of key figures. He equally points to risks of using single parameters due to their own inaccuracies as well as their exposure to manipulation and fabrication by editors and other significant actors. Finally, in part four, Lars Engwall, Uppsala University, elaborates on the quality of quality assessment, with empirical examples pointing to the risks of rejecting important papers as well as accepting fraudulent ones. He also calls attention to increasing difficulties for editors to get colleagues to accept review work.

The fifth part focuses on the particular problems with bibliometric exercises in the humanities and the social sciences. Milena Žic Fuchs from the University of Zagreb deals with the specific problems of bibliometrics in the humanities. She particularly points to the disregard of books, edited volumes and articles in national languages that are common in the humanities. The chapter also presents efforts to handle these problems. In a subsequent chapter, Frederik Verleysen, Pol Ghesquière and Tim Engels, from the University of Antwerp and the University of Leuven, present a database of accredited journals and publishers that was commissioned by the Flemish government in order to include the humanities and the social sciences in benchmarking. They describe the objectives and the design of the system as well as its current content and problems associated with it. They draw a revealing comparison with similar enterprises in three Nordic countries. In the final chapter, Stéphanie Chatelain-Ponroy (Conservatoire National des Arts et Métiers), Stéphanie Mignot-Gérard (Université Paris-Est Créteil), Christine Musselin (Sciences Po) and Samuel Sponem (HEC Montreal) present the results from studies of indicators in French universities, thereby making comparisons between institutions oriented towards the humanities and the social sciences, on one hand, and natural science-oriented institutions, on the other. They find the use and acceptance of the indicators to be higher among natural scientists than in the humanities and the social sciences.

Finally, the editors present some conclusions from the earlier chapters, in the light of both the origins of bibliometrics and of the most recent discussions. We sum them up with ten recommendations. With that we wish readers an enjoyable and stimulating reading of the following chapters. In case you find it appropriate to cite the volume and the contributions therein, we would of course not mind…

References

1. Blaug, M. (1976) Human capital theory: a slightly jaundiced survey. *Journal of Economic Literature* **14**, 827–855
2. Whitley, R., Gläser, J. and Engwall, L. (2010) *Reconfiguring Knowledge Production: Changing Authority Relationships in the Sciences and their Consequences for Intellectual Innovation.* Oxford University Press, Oxford

3. Shatz, D. (2004) *Peer Review: A Critical Inquiry*. Rowman & Littlefield, Lanham, MD
4. Drori, G.S., Meyer, J.W., Ramirez, F.O. and Schofer, E. (2003) *Science in the Modern World Polity: Institutionalization and Globalization*. Stanford University Press, CA
5. Ernst, R.R. (2010) The follies of citation indices and academic ranking lists. A brief commentary to 'Bibliometrics as weapons of mass citation'. *Chimia* **64**, 90
6. Engwall, L. (2014) Corporate governance and communication. In *Organizations and the Media. Organizing in a Mediatized World* (Pallas, J., Strannegård, L. and Jonsson, S., eds), pp. 220–233, Routledge, London
7. Lindroth, S. (1976) *A History of Uppsala University 1477–1977*, pp. 12–15, Uppsala University, Uppsala
8. Ruegg, W. (1992) Themes. In *A History of the University in Europe Volume I* (de Ridder-Symoens, H., ed.), pp. 14–20, Cambridge University Press, Cambridge
9. Hammerstein, N. (1996) Relations with authority. In *A History of the University in Europe Volume II* (de Ridder-Symoens, H., ed.), pp. 113–124, Cambridge University Press, Cambridge
10. DiMaggio, P.J. and Powell, W.W. (1983) The iron cage revisited: institutional isomorphism and collective rationality in organizational fields. *American Sociology Review* **48**, 147–160
11. Wedlin, L. (2006) *Ranking Business Schools: Forming Fields, Identities, and Boundaries in International Management Education*. Edward Elgar, Cheltenham

2

Science, problem-solving and bibliometrics

Giuseppe Longo[1,2]
Centre Cavaillès, République des Savoirs, CNRS, Collège de France et Ecole Normale Supérieure, Paris, France

Problems and theories

The head of a prestigious scientific institution recently said, paraphrasing a famous quotation, "We solve problems that are posed, not that we pose". This view totally misses the history and role of human knowledge construction and prepares wrong ways for evaluating it. Science is not problem-solving, it is theory-building. Any relevant difficult problem requires the construction of a new theoretical frame to deal with the problem in an original and effective way. Moreover, problems follow from the proposal of a theory.

Animals continually solve problems that are posed to them by events. We, humans, using language of our communicating society, looked at the Moon and the Stars, which pose no problem, and invented myths and theories, and derived from them countless problems. We also looked at inert matter, a stone and some sand on a Greek beach, and proposed the atomistic theory. Science emerged from these attempts to organize the world by concepts and theories. Later, it was radically renewed by looking again at planets, but from a different perspective: from the point of view of the sun, on the grounds of a different metaphysics, which led to a theoretical revolution. It was also renewed by looking at two falling stones in an original way and at physical trajectories as inertial, at the infinite limit of a non-existing frictionless movement.

As a matter of fact, science is not the progressive occupation of reality by known tools, it is instead the definition of the very objects of knowledge, the construction of new perspectives and new conceptual frames. Problems that follow from these active constructions of knowledge, interact with it. Relevant problems, posed within a given theory, require a new insight, a change of perspective and often a new theory. And in the history of science, theories can hardly be distinguished from philosophical thinking. This may be implicit, but further novelties and critical reflections are enhanced by explicit philosophical frames, sometimes also in interaction with the arts and their proper knowledge content and expression [1–3]. This interplay is at the core of the history of mathematics, physics and biology; it reached a very high intensity in some of the most productive moments of our cultural and scientific invention, the 6th–4th Centuries BCE in Greece, the Italian Renaissance and during the decades of formation of 20th Century mathematics, physics and biology, bridging the last two centuries.

[1]Email: giuseppe.longo@ens.fr
[2]Papers by Longo in the present chapter may be downloaded from http://www.di.ens.fr/users/longo/

In contrast with this, one prominent physicist once stated that, "the philosophy of science is about as useful to scientists as ornithology is to birds". And birds are very good at solving their problems. Yet, can one set apart the philosophy of knowledge and of science from the theoretical ideas of Darwin, Riemann, Poincaré, Bohr, Einstein, Schrödinger etc.? As a matter of fact, in the minds of most managers of science, this critique of philosophy also covers the theoretical aspects of science, as they always border on each other. So governments' policies in financing science must be justified by their role in solving the country's problems and by their accountable economic fall-out, as stated the French *Cour des Comptes* (the constitutional Accounting Agency) a few years ago. In either case, science, with no philosophy, is viewed as applied problem-solving, with immediate or short-term economic results. This misses the actual role and history of culture and science, which radically modified the human condition. Science and culture crucially contributed, often by 'enabling' in a highly unpredictable way and in changing economic and social contexts, the dynamics of our societies.

Going back to birds, ornithology is the science of bird life and evolution; it is then analogous to knowledge and reflections on the human condition and history. Subsequently, the difference between birds and humans is exactly that birds do not have ornithology, whereas we have 'humanology', that is humanities and a theory of human evolution (or natural sciences, more generally).

Bibliometrics and democracy

Managers continually solve problems that are posed to them, of whatever kind. They have a general training that teaches them how to solve problems in any context, by referring to a unique universal theory: the 'common sense' theory.

Today, managers have stepped into science by solving a fundamental problem: how to evaluate science? How to finance it? So they have used the common sense theory: by asking the vote of the majority of scientists, in each discipline. This vote is expressed by the number of citations and by the impact factors of journals, based on the (average) number of citations in the 2 years following publication. Isn't this an unquestionable and effective use of democracy? Since this poll, in comparative evaluations, is directly and indirectly expressed by counting quotations, it is, allegedly, a rigorous expression of a majority consensus. It is objective.

At present, democracy is grounded on two fundamental principles: the government by a majority and the possibility for a minority to propose alternative policies, to explore new or different ways of being together.

The formation of scientific thinking is a delicate process. Science is the interplay between these two fundamental aspects of democracy. When some major theory becomes common sense, then novelty will pop out against this common sense framework, by a disagreement with the mainframe theory. This has been so since the formation of Greek science, then with the modern scientific revolution and further on with the 20th Century radical changes of perspective, in physics, mathematics and biology. The formation of scientific knowledge is always against 'common sense' [4].

Also, in everyday work and in relation to existing theories, a scientific thinker always starts with a 'dissatisfaction'. In mathematics, say, facing a problem, the relevant solution comes from saying first: the mathematical structures that are currently used for this or that are not good ones, this is not the right theoretical approach, these are not the right tools. Then, the mathematician looks at matters from an ever so slightly different perspective, in a new frame. Dissatisfaction helps in 'taking a step to the side', reflecting critically on the current approaches, inventing new mathematical structures, maybe minor variants of existing ones.

Critical thinking is at the core of scientific theorizing: one has to step aside and look at the very principles of knowledge construction, as grounding the dominating way of thinking. And change fuels the history of science. We have to be constantly mobile, plastic, adaptive and able to get away from the dominating frame. But also an engineer who has had good theoretical and critical training may face a technical problem posed to him/her, by proposing a new point of view, by approaching it in a new way, away from the intended applied frame or theory and, by this, he/she may invent an unexpected solution. On the theoretical side, a way for enhancing a critique of leading knowledge principles and exploring new scientific perspectives may involve the crossing of boundaries, comparing foundations and an explicit philosophical commitment in natural sciences [5,6].

Critical thinking is the fundamental component of minority thinking: it implies disagreement with respect to the mainframe theory, the common sense theory. This forces science to relate to democracy by relying first on the minority side, by the proposal of new ways of understanding, acting and moving forward. This is so also in ordinary research activity, possibly through minor changes of perspective, otherwise it is not scientific research. Sometimes, rarely, changes are revolutionary; always, they enrich knowledge and prepare revolutions.

Of course, one may work in the 'majority theory', but the novelty, the new idea, even within that theory, will always require a change of insight that will place the proponent on a critical side, possibly a new minority side, more or less away from the mainframe. History of science teaches us that the opinion of the majority has always been on the wrong side, at each moment of the formation of new scientific thinking. One does not need to refer only to the most quoted turning points, such as the modern scientific revolution, as it was also for the early approaches to biological evolution (Buffon and Lamarck), or for differential geometry and the various branches of physics invented in the 19th Century (thermodynamics, electromagnetism and statistical physics). Gauss was 'afraid' to present his ideas on non-Euclidean geometry and did not make them public for decades. Riemann and Helmholtz were literally insulted by the award winner E. Dühring, elected by influential majorities in 1872, about 20 years after Riemann's fundamental writings on differential geometry. Poincaré's geometry of non-linear systems was largely ignored for about 60 years, until the 1950s, when theories of deterministic chaos were brought to the limelight by Kolmogoroff and Lorentz. Some work I recently studied, Turing's seminal paper on morphogenesis [7], had little or no followers for about 20 years! An early revitalization can be found in the paper by Fox-Keller and Segel [8].

These are not exceptions: this is how scientific thought is formed. The exception is when an innovative theory is quickly accepted: Einstein's relativity theory is probably the unique case of a rapid success and diffusion of a novel approach. I am not expressing this as the romantic myth of the isolated revolutionary scientist. These revolutions or novelties are always made possible by and within strong scientific schools. The modern scientific revolution matured in the intellectually very lively context of the Italian renaissance. It crossed the invention of perspective in painting, a new organization of human space, including, later, the spaces of astronomy [2,3,9]. Naturalism originated then in a new way of looking at phenomena and at our humanity, by inventing a new metaphysics, from Leonardo's drawings to Nicolas Cusanus's proposal of an 'infinite universe' [10]. These processes always required a change of viewpoint, with respect to the official theory, also within an excellent school, yet against that very school.

Galileo, in his youth, worked on the 'physics of Hell' [11], a possible path towards the 'naturalization' of a religious ontology and, by this, of knowledge. As a matter of fact, a common fashion in the 16th Century was for excellent physicists and mathematicians, the heirs of Pacioli, Cardano and Bombelli, to solve the many problems posed by the material structure of Hell. Galileo turned one of these problems into a seminal theory, that is, into science. Note that Hell is a cone of a 60° base angle, whose vertex is at the centre of the Earth. This poses a major challenge, dear to the Church's and Universities' managers of the time, who wanted scientists to solve problems and claimed to be opened to the new sciences: how thick must the Earth's arch be to cover Hell as a dome? In order to obtain an estimate of this value, Galileo referred to the structural properties of Brunelleschi's dome of Santa Maria del Fiore. But he did not use its ratio of sizes, instead he made an original computation using his intuition on the scaling effects. While he obtains, as for the thickness of the Hell's roof, one height of the Earth's radius, he observes that a small dome of 30 'braccia' (arm length) may be only one or even one-half braccio [11]. Galileo was also puzzled by the scaling of the Devil, a further challenge, as she is 1200 metres tall, with the same proportions of a human, and thus impossible (for a historical discussion and a possible solution to the now widely accepted 'Devil's violation of scaling equations', see [12,13]). This problem opened the way to Galileo's seminal work on scaling and its fundamental equations 50 years later, which extends also to biology: the section of bones gives their strength; it must thus grow like the cube of their length, not as the square, since the animal's weight grows like the cube [14] (also see Chapter 2 in [6]). The paths of knowledge construction are unpredictable and may even pass through Hell [13] if a scientist is allowed to think theoretically and with sufficient freedom, that is, to deal with a problem by theory-building, in full scientific generality.

This juvenile work gave Galileo a sufficient bibliometric index to get tenure in Pisa in 1589, when he stopped working on Hell and, some time later, got in touch with Kepler. Tenure is fundamental to the exercise of free thinking, even though, in some historical contexts, it may be insufficient to protect this freedom when the novel theoretical proposal is too audacious and too much against the mainstream, and minority thinking (thus scientific thinking) is not allowed to go beyond certain metaphysical or political limits.

In this case and in all of the others I have mentioned above, the new theoretical frame emerges within a strong scientific school and a relatively free debate, it is allowed to emerge as long as the novelty does not contradict a dominating metaphysics. Yet, even within a school, further change is ascribable to a few who dare to go further, or, more precisely, to think differently. It is the school that produces the possibility of thinking deeply and differently, it is not a matter of isolated individualities.

We have to promote schools, but their strength will reside also in the amount of freedom they grant to side-track approaches. No one could think freely in the Soviet Union, except in mathematics and in theoretical physics (but not in biology) within the Academy of Sciences. Yet, remarkable and original work in mathematics and physics was produced in that singular context. Some local space of dissent may suffice for science if circumstances allow (for example, the social privileges accorded to scientists in the Soviet Union). But dissent is necessary for science.

Bibliometrics is the apparently 'democratic' analogue of the Church's dominating metaphysics in the 17th Century or the Party's truth in the Soviet Union. These rulers were not elected, but other majority rulers were elected, such as Hitler or Salazar. It suffices then to kill the opposing ideas and democracy loses its meaning, and science disappears, as in Germany after 1933. The majority vote *per se* is not democracy. Democracy also crucially requires the enablement or even the promotion of a thinking and active minority. Bibliometrics forbids minority thinking, where new scientific ideas always occur by definition, as history teaches us. If a scientist has to write his/her bibliometric indices on top of his/her CV, that is, the evaluation by the majority of scientists of his/her work, and present it on all occasions, this will prevent the search for a different approach, the courage to explore a new path that may require 60, 20 or 10 years to be quoted, as in the examples I gave above. And he/she is constantly pushed to develop technical tools in a familiar and well-established theoretical frame as much as possible, as they may allow others to write more papers, where the technique may be quoted.

We all need to be evaluated in science, and ruthlessly. But a new idea, an apparently absurd exploration may be accepted by a majority of two or three in a committee of three or five colleagues giving tenure. Success may require several applications, but the candidate with overly original ideas may finally encounter a small group of open-minded colleagues, who do not look *a priori* at the bibliometric index, but dare to understand and evaluate contents. This also applies to publishing in good journals. If the editor does not care of the expected impact factor of the journal (a 'next 2 years' quotation criterion!), but is able to find open-minded referees, an apparently strange nonsense or non-common-sense idea may find its way to publication. So, even after six or more attempts, the 1971 seminal paper by Ruelle and Takens [15] on chaotic dynamics could find a publisher, and after several years of failures, in the 1990s, unexpected results on 'mirror neurons' by Gallese, Rizzolati and collaborators[3] were at last published [16,17]. Both papers were too original to be immediately accepted, yet a couple of audacious editors finally dared to publish them.

If instead each evaluation refers to a 'global' majority vote, that is, to the opinion expressed by the largest number of quotations or expected quotations (the short-term impact factor) by all scientists in the discipline on earth, science is doomed. Or we will have a new form of techno-science, the kind that managers can easily judge

---

[3]David Ruelle mentioned this story in several lectures. Regarding Vittorio Gallese, this was personal communication.

and finance: short-term problem-solving and techniques within clearly established frames, the problems that the majority in a discipline can easily understand, that even managers can grasp. But no radically new theory will ever pose its own, internal problems that *cannot even be seen* from the dominating perspective.

Networks, diversity and 'the norm'

Computer networks give us a tool comparable with writing, another of our extraordinary inventions. They were both motivated by metaphysics and philosophy. In Mesopotamia, 5000 years ago, humans made visible the invisible, language and thought, in a dialogue with the Gods [18]. Human interaction was suddenly enriched by this new tool and by the magic of the permanent sign, thus the explicitly symbolic transmission of myths, history and knowledge. A new form of exchange modified our communicating community.

In the last century, Hilbert's philosophical questions, originating from his theory on the foundations of mathematics, were answered by Gödel, Church, Kleene and Turing in their proposal of Computability Theory and abstract Logical Computing Machines (Turing). Later, our interacting humanity connected concrete computing machines in networks and started a search for suitable theories of this new level of communication. Networks, present day computer networks in particular, allow mankind to access knowledge and memory of mankind, an extraordinary enhancement of our interactive thinking. We can access diversity, collaborate at a distance, appreciate differences, enrich cultures by endless hybridizations.

Yet, these networks may also be used also for 'normalizing' humanity. They may be used for averaging everybody. Just force a unique criterion for 'excellence'; replace the network structure by a totally ordered line of values, a uniform scale of points, the same for everybody. Then the networks' richness in confronting diversity may be used to forbid any variance from the imposed norm. Transform the network of exchange of universities or of researchers into a total order, on the grounds of a few (often perfectly stupid or managerial) criteria, and diversity is lost.

Hybridization and contamination are at the origin of most novelties in evolution, both biological and human or cultural evolution. But no hybridization or contamination is possible in the absence of diversity, including the 'hopeful monsters', the wrong paths continually explored by phylogenesis [19,20]. We have to accommodate errors, wrong paths, if we want diversity and, by it and within it, the novelty of science.

Self-appointed agencies of managers propose criteria and technical tools for averaging the world of knowledge, to normalize thinking according to common sense values. Many of us signed strong documents against forms of evaluation of scientific work handled by these methods (for an example of one of them, see [21]). We should oppose the proposal of a unique scale of values, some sort of 'index of diversity'. They are already used by biologists to assess the dynamics of an ecosystem: when diversity decreases, the situation generally worsens; major extinctions happen or are expected. Diversity guarantees the ever-changing dynamics that is essential to life and to human cultures. By normalizing evaluations, forcing identity of aims, of metrics and, thus of cultural contents, we are killing the permanent 'variations on themes' as well as the radical changes in perspective that constitute the ever-changing path of scientific knowledge.

Networks allow collaborations, today as never before. Yet, they may be used to force competition mainly on the grounds of fixed values and observables, by accounting criteria with no content. Competition within science is much easier than collaboration. It may even be based on cheating, on announcing false results, declaring non-existing experimental protocols, on stealing results, organizing networks of reciprocal, yet fake quotations. Collaboration instead is very hard: good scientists are very selective in accepting collaborators, and diversity makes the dialogue difficult while producing the most relevant novelties. A research activity mainly based on competing for projects and prizes, on competitive evaluations, destroys the chances for open collaborations, closes the mind to the others. Occasionally, we may need to compete for a job or a grant. The point is to avoid turning this inevitable fact of life into the main attitude in scientific work, that is, to make competition and normalizing evaluations the driving force and the guidelines of our scientific activity, which instead should be based on collaborating diversities.

References

1. Weyl, H. (1952) *Symmetry*. Princeton University Press, Princeton
2. Angelini, A. and Lupacchini, R. (2013) *The Art of Science: Exploring Symmetries Between the Renaissance and Quantum Physics*. Springer, Dordrecht
3. Longo, G. (2011) Mathematical infinity "in prospettiva" and the spaces of possibilities. *Visible* **9**, 35–44
4. Bachelard, G. (1940) *La Philosophie du non*. PUF, Paris
5. Bailly, F. and Longo, G. (2011) *Mathematics and the Natural Sciences: The Physical Singularity of Life*. Imperial College Press, London
6. Longo, G. and Montévil, M. (2013) *Perspectives on Organisms: Biological Time, Symmetries and Singularities*. Springer, Dordrecht
7. Turing, A.M. (1952) The chemical basis of morphogenesis. *Philo. Trans. Royal Soc. B* **237**, 37–72
8. Fox-Keller, E. and Segel, L.A. (1970) Initiation of slime mold aggregation viewed as an instability. *Journal of Theoretical Biology* **26**, 399–415
9. van Fraassen, B.C. (1970) *An Introduction to the Philosophy of Space and Time*. Random House, New York
10. Zellini, P. (2005) *A Brief History of Infinity*. Peguin Books, New York
11. Galilei, G. (1588) Due lezioni circa la figura, sito e grandezza dell'Inferno di Dante; Galileo Galilei, *Scritti* (A. Chiari, ed., 1970) Le Monnier, Florence
12. Lévy-Leblond, J.M. (2006) *La Vitesse de l'ombre. Aux Limites de la Science*. Seuil, Paris
13. Lévy-Leblond, J.M. (2008) De l'Enfer de Dante au Purgatoire de la science. Postface aux 'Deux leçons sur l'Enfer de Dante' (Galilei, 1588), trad. L. Degryse, pp. 137–175, Fayard, Paris
14. Galilei, G. (1638) *Discorsi e dimostrazioni matematiche, intorno a due nuove scienze*
15. Ruelle, D. and Takens, F. (1971) On the nature of turbulence. *Communications in Mathematical Physics* **20**, 167–192; **23**, 343–344
16. Gallese, V., Fadiga, L., Fogassi, L. and Rizzolatti, G. (1996) Action recognition in the premotor cortex. *Brain* **119**, 593–609
17. Rizzolati, G., Gentilucci, M., Camarda, R.M. et al. (1990) Neurons related to reach-grasping arm movements in the rostral part of area 6 (area 6a β). *Experimental Brain Search* **82**, 67–89
18. Herrenschmidt, C. (2007) *Les Trois Écritures*. Gallimard, Paris
19. Goldschmidt, R. (1940) *The Material Basis of Evolution*. Yale University Press, New Haven
20. Gould, S.J. (1989) *Wonderful Life*. Norton & Co., London
21. Editors, Bibliometrics and the curators of orthodoxy (2009) *Mathematical Structure in Computer Science* **19**, 1–4; also available at: http://www.di.ens.fr/users/longo/files/editorsMSCS.pdf

PART II: INSTRUMENTS OF MEASUREMENT

3

Advances in bibliometric analysis: research performance assessment and science mapping

Anthony F.J. van Raan[1]

Centre for Science and Technology Studies, Leiden University, The Netherlands

Introduction

The daily practice of scientific research shows that inspired scientists, particularly in the natural sciences and medical research fields, go for publication in international journals[2] (see [1]). Certainly, journal articles are not in all fields the main carrier of scientific knowledge, and they differ widely in importance. But work of at least some importance provokes reactions of colleagues. They are the 'invisible college' by which research results are discussed, and they play their role as members of the invisible college by referring in their own work to earlier work of other scientists. This process of citation is a complex one, and it does not provide an 'ideal' monitor of scientific performance. This is particularly the case at a statistically low aggregation level, e.g. the individual researcher. But the application of citation analysis to the work, the oeuvre of a group of researchers as a whole over a longer period of time, does yield, in many situations, a strong indicator of scientific performance. For a very long time, the Science Citation Index, now the WoS (Web of Science) (produced by Thomson Reuters) was the only large multidisciplinary citation data source worldwide. Meanwhile, Scopus, produced by Elsevier, is a second comprehensive citation database.

The motives for giving (or not giving) a reference to a particular article may vary considerably. There is, however, no empirical evidence that these reference motives are so different or randomly given to such an extent that the phenomenon of citation would lose its role as a reliable measure of impact [2].

Why bibliometric analysis of research performance? Peer review is and has to remain the principal procedure of quality judgment. But peer review may have serious shortcomings and disadvantages. Subjectivity, i.e. dependence of the outcomes on the choice of individual committee members, is one of the major problems. This dependence may result in conflicts of interests, unawareness of quality or a negative bias against younger people or newcomers to the field. To make peer review more objective and transparent, it should be supported by advanced bibliometric methods.

My institute [CWTS (Centre for Science and Technology Studies), Leiden University] has long-standing experience of more than 25 years in developing and applying standardized bibliometric procedures based on citation analysis for assessing research performance in an international context. We analysed the research

[1]Email: vanraan@cwts.leidenuniv.nl.
[2]This chapter is partly an elaborated version of an earlier paper by the author [1].

performance of hundreds of research groups, departments and institutes worldwide. Client institutions for this contract work are universities, research councils, research organizations, ministries, charities and business companies. As discussed above, this approach does not provide us an ideal instrument, working perfectly in all fields under all circumstances. But it works very well in the large majority of the natural, the medical, the applied and the behavioural sciences. These fields of science are the most cost-intensive and the ones with the strongest socio-economic impact.

A first and good indication of whether bibliometric analysis is applicable to a specific field is provided by the publication characteristics of the field, in particular, the role of international refereed journals. If international journals are a major means of communication in a field, then in most cases bibliometric analysis is applicable. Therefore it is important to study the publication practices of a research group, department or institute, in order to find out whether bibliometric analysis can be applied reliably. A practical measure to this end is the share of publications covered by the WoS or by Scopus in the total research output. For 'non-WoS publications', a restricted type of analysis is possible, in so far as these publications are cited by articles in journals covered by the WoS. This approach is particularly important for bibliometric analysis in the social sciences and humanities [3]. But given the limited journal coverage of the WoS in these disciplines, this approach will only provide first indications.

The Internet has changed scientific communication. Researchers use the web for both information-seeking as well as presenting. In addition to the non-WoS publications, there are a large number of further publications and data included in institutional and personal websites. Thus next to citation analysis, the use of data provided via the Internet, *webometrics*, offers interesting additional opportunities to aid citation-based bibliometric analysis in evaluation and mapping approaches.

Basics of citation analysis

The basic principle of bibliometric analysis is the citation network. The two main bibliometric methods, citation analysis for research performance assessment and science mapping, can both be derived from the same network principle. A simple example of the citation network structure is shown in Figure 1. Citation analysis for research performance assessment basically means counting citations of specific papers, for instance paper pb1 is cited three times (by pa1, pa2 and pa3). From the primary network two secondary networks can be derived, the CC (co-citation) and the BC (bibliographic coupling) network. Two publications are bibliographically coupled if they have references in common; the more references they have in common, the stronger their relation (BC strength). Two publications are co-cited if they are commonly cited by other papers. The more papers a specific pair of papers cite, the stronger the CC strength.

The strength of the relations between publications provides similarity measures and thus the possibility to cluster so that both BC and CC can be used for mapping. With the BC method we can create maps on the basis of publications in their *citing* modality, and in the CC method the maps are on the basis of the *cited* modality. As the citing modality cannot be changed anymore (the references

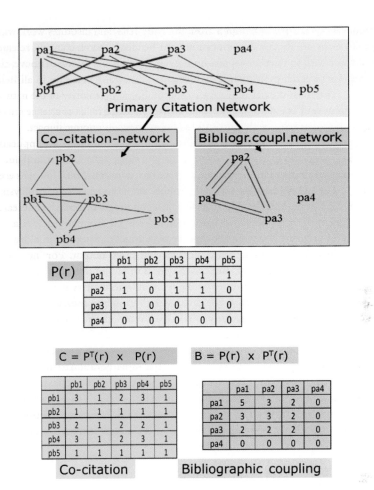

Figure 1

The citation network

The primary citation network consists of four publications (pa1–pa4) that cite the publications pb1–pb5 in the way shown. From this primary citation network we can deduce two secondary networks: one is the CC network and the other is the BC network. In the CC network the strength between, for instance, pb1 and pb4 is 3 because there are three publications that cite pb1 and pb4 together (namely pa1, pa2 and pa3). In the BC network the strength between, for instance, pa2 and pa3 is 2 because these publications have two cited publications in common (namely pb1 and pb4). The lower panel is the same network, but in matrix form. Using matrix algebra, we denote the primary network as matrix P(r); the CC network is created by pre-multiplying P(r) with its transpose matrix P^T(r), and the BC network is created by post-multiplying P(r) with P^T(r).

in publications are fixed and thus remain the same), the BC maps are static, whereas the CC maps are dynamic (publications can be cited later on, again and again). I will come back to science mapping in the next section. I will first discuss citation analysis for research-performance assessment.

The most crucial objective in the bibliometric methodology is to find a consistent and standardized set of indicators. Research output is defined as the number of articles of the institute, as far as they are covered by the WoS (or Scopus). I consider as 'articles' the following publication types: normal articles (including proceedings papers published in journals), letters, notes and reviews (but not meeting abstracts, obituaries, corrections, editorials, etc.).

The basic indicators, number of publications and citations, are illustrated by Figure 2. For the outsider this looks like 'just counting numbers'. But the reliable establishment of even these two basic indicators is far from trivial. Verification is crucial in order to remove errors and to detect incompleteness of addresses of research organizations, departments, groups, and to assure correct assignment of publications to research groups and completeness of publications sets. My institute developed standardized procedures for carrying out the analysis as conscientiously as possible. These procedures are discussed thoroughly beforehand with the institutes concerned. The data analysis is carried out with the CWTS bibliometric database, which is an improved and enriched version of the WoS database.

In the example in Figure 2, a university department has 500 publications in the period 2008–2012 ($P = 500$). Within the same period, these publications are cited 3000 times ($C = 3000$). The average citation impact of the department is $cd = 6$. How do we know that a certain number of citations or a certain value of citations per publication is low or high? To answer this question we have to make a comparison with (i.e. normalization to) an international reference value. For this normalization we use a similar measure for:

1. *All journals used by the department*, the journal impact average is $cj = 4$ (measured in the same 5-year period and taking article type into account).
2. *All journals in all fields where the department is active*, the field average is $cf = 3$ (again measured in the same 5-year period and taking article type into account).

Figure 2

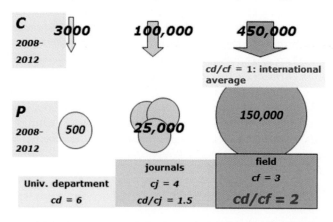

Basic indicators

Research groups publish in more than one journal, and they are active in more than one field. Therefore weighted average values are calculated, the weights being determined by the total number of papers published by the institute in each journal or field.

We observed the following. The department performs better than both the journal and the field average (cd/cj = 1.5; cd/cf = 2.0); and the journals chosen by the department for publications are the better ones in the fields (cj/cf = 1.3). We call cd/cf our 'crown indicator' because this indicator directly measures the extent to which a research group, department, institute, etc. performs significantly above the international level. The above indicators are a simple representation of the normalization procedure. In reality it is somewhat more complicated [4]. Given the skewness of the distribution of citations over publications, we increasingly apply indicators related to the entire citation distribution.[3]

As a real-life example I show in Table 1 the main bibliometric indicators for the LUMC (Leiden University Medical Centre). There is ample empirical evidence that in the natural and life sciences, basic as well as applied, the average 'peak' in the number of citations is in the third or fourth year after publication. Therefore a 4-year period is appropriate for impact assessment. A trend analysis is based on successive and partially overlapping 4-year periods, as presented in Table 1.

I remarked above that we apply a more advanced normalization procedure. But in good approximation, MCS is the same as cd, $MNCS$ is the same as cd/cf (and thus our crown indicator) and $MNJS$ is the same as cj/cf. Indicator $\%Pnc$ is the percentage of publications not cited. I stress that this percentage of non-cited papers concerns, similar to all other indicators, the given time period. It is possible that publications not cited within such a time period will be cited after a longer time ('Sleeping Beauties' [5]). In the last column $\%Scit$ is the percentage of self-citations in the total number of citations. Notice that all other indicators are corrected for self-citations.

We see that LUMC performs very well above the international level ($MNCS$ = 1.64 in the last period). With an $MNCS$ value above 1.5, such as in this example, the institute can be considered to be scientifically strong. Usually the analysis is continued at a lower aggregation level, i.e. the department and research

Table 1
Trend analysis of bibliometric indicators, LUMC, 2000–2010

LUMC	P (n)	C (n)	MCS	%Pnc	MNCS	MNJS	%Scit
2000–2003	4146	45643	8.76	16	1.38	1.28	20
2001–2004	4247	49057	9.17	14	1.41	1.28	21
2002–2005	4422	50595	9.03	13	1.37	1.28	21
2003–2006	4738	54777	9.10	13	1.37	1.29	21
2004–2007	4967	64551	10.35	12	1.44	1.30	20
2005–2008	5360	70540	10.43	11	1.51	1.31	21
2006–2009	5522	76001	10.89	12	1.54	1.36	21
2007–2010	5871	85733	11.47	11	1.64	1.43	21

[3]See the methodology section of the latest version of the Leiden Ranking at: http://www. leidenranking.com/

groups within an institute; see for instance my institute's work for Uppsala University [6].

On the basis of my institute's long-standing experience with biblio-metric indicators, we recently created an advanced menu-driven application tool for bibliometric research performance assessment and monitoring of university departments and institutes, including geographical maps with indication of research groups worldwide citing and/or collaborating with the institutes under study.[4] Also we developed a free-access advanced journal indicator application tool based on Scopus data of approximately 20 000 journals.[5]

In citation analysis pitfalls and sources of error lurk. Methodological and technical problems have to be solved in order to conduct a bibliometric analysis properly [1]. Given the limited space available in this chapter, I mention briefly a number of important and topical issues with references to relevant literature.

1. Effects of *language*, particularly German and French on the assessment of research performance and on the ranking of universities [7,8].
2. Important publications may be *cited after many years*, known as 'delayed recognition' or *Sleeping Beauties* [5].
3. *Statistical properties* of bibliometric indicators, for instance their skewness and scaling behaviour [9–12].
4. Effects of *self-citations* on 'external' citations [13].
5. Relation between *peer review* judgment and bibliometric findings [14].
6. Effects of *open access* on citation impact [15].
7. Field-independent normalization procedures: *source normalized impact per paper* (or SNIP) [16].
8. Bibliometric analysis in the *social sciences and humanities* [17].
9. Methodological and technical problems of *university rankings* [8,18].
10. Inconsistency of the *h-index* (Hirsch-index) [19].
11. Inappropriateness of the *journal impact factor* (or JIF) for research-performance assessment [20].

All the above issues play crucial roles in the careful application of bibliometric indicators. I stress that these issues were and still are important themes within the research programmes of CWTS and other bibliometric research groups. I continue this chapter with a discussion of the second main bibliometric method: science mapping.

Science mapping

Each year approximately 1 million scientific articles are published. How can we keep track of all these developments? Are there specific patterns hidden in this mass of published knowledge at a meta-level, and if so, how can these patterns be interpreted? I return to the citation network in Figure 1, where I explained

---

[4]See CWTS website at: http://www.socialsciences.leiden.edu/cwts/
[5]See CWTS journal indicators website at: http://www.journalindicators.com/

how this network forms the basis of science mapping. Instead of publications characterized by a *list of references* (the cited publications), imagine that the same publications are also characterized by a *list of keywords*. Then, we can construct networks mathematically similar to CC analysis, but now it is *co-word analysis*.

My institute's science mapping methodology uses this co-word analysis to visualize scientific fields. The development of co-word maps has a 30-year history. A co-word map is a two-dimensional representation of a field in which strongly related terms are located close to each other and less strongly related terms are located further away from each other. A co-word map thus provides an overview of the structure of a field. Different areas in a map correspond with different subfields or research areas.

The first methodological step is the definition of scientific fields. My institute uses the (WoS-based) CWTS bibliometric database. This database has good coverage of particularly the natural sciences and medical fields and is a long-standing data source for professional bibliometric analyses. In particular, we use the WoS journal subject categories to define fields. There are about 250 subject categories in the WoS database, covering fields in the natural sciences and medicine, the social sciences, and the arts and humanities.

Using natural language processing techniques, titles and abstracts of the publications in a field are parsed. This yields a list of all noun phrases (i.e. sequences of nouns and adjectives) that occur in these publications. An additional algorithm selects the 2000 noun phrases that can be regarded as the most characteristic terms of the field [21,22]. This algorithm filters out general noun phrases, for instance 'result', 'study', 'patient' and 'clinical evidence'. Filtering out these general noun phrases is crucial. Owing to their general meaning, these noun phrases do not relate specifically to one topic, and they therefore tend to distort the structure of a co-word map. Apart from excluding general noun phrases, noun phrases that occur only in a small number of publications are excluded as well. This is done in order to obtain sufficiently robust results. The minimum number of publications in which a noun phrase must occur depends on the total number of publications in a field. In most cases, we use thresholds between 70 and 135 publications.

Given a selection of 2000 terms that together characterize a field, the next step is to determine the number of publications in which each pair of terms co-occurs. Two terms are said to co-occur in a publication if they both occur at least once in the title or abstract of the publication. The larger the number of publications in which two terms co-occur, the stronger the terms are considered to be related to each other. In neuroscience, for instance, 'Alzheimer' and 'short-term memory' may be expected to co-occur a lot, indicating a strong relation between these two terms. The matrix of term co-occurrence frequencies serves as input for the VOS mapping technique [21,22]. This technique determines for each term a location in a two-dimensional space. Strongly related terms tend to be located close to each other in the two-dimensional space, whereas terms that do not have a strong relation are located further away from each other. The VOS mapping technique is closely related to the technique of multidimensional scaling, but for the purpose of creating co-word maps the VOS mapping technique has been shown to yield more satisfactory results. It is important to note that in the interpretation of a co-word map, only the distances between terms are relevant. A map can be freely rotated because this does not affect the inter-term distances. This also implies that the horizontal and vertical axes have no special meaning.

A fascinating next step is the combination of the two bibliometric methods, citation analysis and mapping. Visualization approaches have not been used before to study differences in citation practices between research areas. My institute's work is the first attempt to create such citation-density maps. To this end, the relative citation impact of each term is determined and indicated with a colour. First, in order to correct for the age of a publication, each publication's number of citations is divided by the average number of citations of all publications that appeared in the same year. This yields a publication's normalized citation score. A score of 1 means that the number of citations of a publication equals the average of all publications that appeared in the same field and in the same year. Next, for each of the 2000 terms, the normalized citation scores of all publications in which the term occurs (in the title or abstract) are averaged. The colour of a term is determined based on the resulting average score. Colours range from blue (average score of 0) to green (average score of 1) to red (average score of 2 or higher). Hence a blue term indicates that the publications in which a term occurs have a low average citation impact, whereas a red term indicates that the underlying publications have a high average citation impact. The VOSviewer software is used to visualize the co-word maps resulting from the above steps.

As an example, I show in Figure 3 the map of neurology. This map is based on all publications (105405 in all!) that are classified as 'article' or 'review' and published between 2006 and 2010 in the WoS field (journal category) 'Clinical Neurology'. For each publication, citations are counted until the end of 2011. We observe striking features. *Clinical research* areas tend to be located mainly on

Figure 3

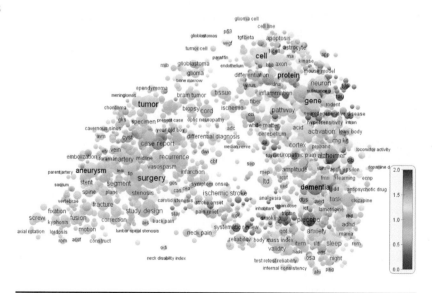

Science map of neurology

Colours indicate local citation density. For a detailed discussion of this map, see [23].

the left-hand side of the map and *basic research* areas mainly on the right-hand side. Connections between basic research areas and clinical research areas are also visible. The maps display 'bridges' that seem to represent *translational research*, that is, research aimed at translating basic research results into clinical practice. Furthermore, the distinction between different research areas is visible not only in the structure of the maps, but also in the colours of the terms. In general, low-impact research areas tend to focus on clinical research, in particular on surgical interventions. Research areas that are more oriented towards basic and diagnostic research usually have an above-average citation impact. We note that within an area in a map, terms are usually coloured in a quite consistent way: terms tend to be surrounded mainly by other terms with a similar colour. This is an important indication of the robustness of the maps.

Concluding remarks

Advanced bibliometric analysis is a powerful method to, first, assess with citation analysis the international influence of scientific work in a reliable, transparent and objective way, particularly in the natural science and medical fields, and in several of the engineering and social science fields; and secondly, discover with science maps patterns in the structure of fields, which enables us to identify interdisciplinarity, knowledge flows such as translational medical research, and research related to important socio-economic issues.

With advanced menu-driven application tools for research performance assessment and monitoring of university departments and institutes, for journal indicators, ranking of universities and mapping, bibliometric methods have now reached a stage of high-quality, reliable and very informative instruments in research evaluation practice.

References

1. van Raan, A.F.J. (2004) Measuring science. Capita selecta of current main issues. In: *Handbook of Quantitative Science and Technology Research* (Moed, H.F., Glänzel, W. and Schmoch, U., eds), pp. 19–50, Kluwer Publishers, Dordrecht
2. van Raan, A.F.J. (1998) In matters of quantitative studies of science the fault of theorists is offering too little and asking too much. *Scientometrics* **43**, 129–139
3. Butler, L. and Visser, M.S. (2006) Extending citation analysis to non-source items. *Scientometrics* **66**, 327–343
4. Waltman, L., van Eck, N.J., van Leeuwen, T.N., Visser, M.S. and van Raan, A.F.J. (2011) Towards a new crown indicator: an empirical analysis. *Scientometrics* **87**, 467–481
5. van Raan, A.F.J. (2004) Sleeping beauties in science. *Scientometrics* **59**, 461–466
6. Uppsala University (2007) Quality and Renewal 2007: An Overall Evaluation of Research at Uppsala University 2006/2007. Also available from: http://uu.diva-portal.org/smash/get/diva2:43034/FULLTEXT01.pdf
7. van Raan, A.F.J., van Leeuwen, T.N. and Visser, M.S. (2011) Severe language effect in university rankings: particularly Germany and France are wronged in citation-based rankings. *Scientometrics* **88**, 495–498
8. Waltman, L., Calero-Medina, C., Kosten, J. et al. (2012) The Leiden Ranking 2011/2012: data collection, indicators, and interpretation. *Journal of the American Society for Information Science and Technology* **63**, 2419–2432. Open access pre-print version: http://arxiv.org/abs/1202.3941

9. van Raan, A.F.J. (2006) Statistical properties of bibliometric indicators: research group indicator distributions and correlations. *Journal of the American Society for Information Science and Technology* **57**, 408–430

10. van Raan, A.F.J. (2006) Performance-related differences of bibliometric statistical properties of research groups: cumulative advantages and hierarchically layered networks. *Journal of the American Society for Information Science and Technology* **57**, 1919–1935

11. van Raan, A.F.J. (2008) Bibliometric statistical properties of the 100 largest European research universities: prevalent scaling rules in the science system. *Journal of the American Society for Information Science and Technology* **59**, 461–475

12. van Raan, A.F.J. (2008) Scaling rules in the science system: influence of field-specific citation characteristics on the impact of research groups. *Journal of the American Society for Information Science and Technology* **59**, 565–576

13. van Raan, A.F.J. (2008) Self-citation as an impact-reinforcing mechanism in the science system. *Journal of the American Society for Information Science and Technology* **59**, 1631–1643

14. Rinia, E.J., van Leeuwen, Th.N., van Vuren, H.G. and van Raan, A.F.J. (1998) Comparative analysis of a set of bibliometric indicators and central peer review criteria. Evaluation of condensed matter physics in The Netherlands. *Research Policy* **27**, 95–107

15. Moed, H.F. (2007) The effect of "Open access" on citation impact: an analysis of ArXiv's condensed matter section. *Journal of the American Society for Information Science and Technology* **58**, 2047–2054

16. Moed, H.F. (2010) Measuring contextual citation impact of scientific journals. *Journal of Informetrics* **4**, 265–277

17. Nederhof, A.J. (2006) Bibliometric monitoring of research performance in the social sciences and the humanities: a review. *Scientometrics* **66**, 81–100

18. van Raan, A.F.J. (2005) Fatal attraction: conceptual and methodological problems in the ranking of universities by bibliometric methods. *Scientometrics* **62**, 133–143

19. Waltman, L. and van Eck, N.J. (2012) The inconsistency of the h-index. *Journal of the American Society for Information Science and Technology* **63**, 406–415. Open access pre-print version: http://arxiv.org/abs/1108.3901

20. van Leeuwen, T.N. (2012) Discussing some basic critique on journal impact factors: revision of earlier comments. *Scientometrics* **92**, 443–455

21. van Eck, N.J. and Waltman, L. (2010) Software survey: VOSviewer, a computer program for bibliometric mapping. *Scientometrics* **84**, 523–538

22. van Eck, N.J. and Waltman, L. (2011) Text mining and visualization using VOSviewer. *ISSI Newsletter* **7**, 50–54

23. van Eck, N.J., Waltman, L., van Raan, A.F.J., Klautz, R.J.M. and Peul, W.C. (2013) Citation analysis may severely underestimate the impact of clinical research as compared to basic research. *PLoS ONE* **8**, e62395

Appendix: overview of bibliometric indicators

P: number of publications in WoS[6]-covered journals of a specific research entity (group, department, institute, university, etc.) in a given time period. All of the following indicators are based on the publications covered by the set *P* of the specific research entity.

C: number of citations without self-citations received by the publications during the given period.

cd: average number of citations per publication without self-citations.

cj: average number of citations per publication without self-citations for each journal used by the research entity (journal impact). Almost always, a research entity uses several journals for its publications (or many, if the entity is large such as a university), and therefore we calculate the weighted average. For this calculation of *cj*, the same publication and citation counting procedure, time windows and article types are used as in the case of *cd*.

cf: average number of citations per publication without self-citations for a whole field, i.e. all the journals of a field together (field impact or field-specific citation density). Almost always, a research entity is active in several fields (or many, if the entity is large such as a university), and therefore we calculate the weighted average *cf*. For this calculation of *cf*, the same publication and citation counting procedure, time windows and article types are used as in the case of *cd*.

cd/cj: journal-specific normalized average number of citations per publication without self-citations, i.e. normalization of the actually received impact *cd* with its world-wide journal-based average *cj*, without self-citations.

cd/cf: field-specific normalized average number of citations per publication without self-citations, i.e. normalization of the actually received impact *cd* with its world-wide field-specific citation density *cf*, without self-citations.

cj/cf: field-specific normalized journal impact indicating whether the impact of a journal is above (*cj/cf* >1) or below (*cj/cf* <1) the field average.

%Pnc: percentage of publications not cited in the given time period.

%Scit: percentage of self-citations.

MCS (mean citation score of a specific research entity)≈*cd*.

MNCS (mean normalized citation score of a specific research entity)≈*cd/cf*.

MNJS (mean normalized journal score of a specific research entity)≈*cj/cf*.

p(top10%): proportion of the publications of a specific entity that, compared with other publications in the same field and in the same year, belong to the top 10% most frequently cited [1].

h-index: a scientist has an h-index with numerical value *h* if *h* of his/her publications each have at least *h* citations, and the remaining publications each have fewer than *h*+1 citations [2]. A simple method for individual scientists to find their h-index is to rank their publications, for instance in the WoS, according to the number of times the publications are cited (starting with the highest cited). Somewhere in this ranking, there will be a publication with a number of citations that is the same as its ranking number. This number is the value of the h-index.

---

[6]WoS, the successor of the Science Citation Index, is produced by Thomson Reuters. All indicators discussed in this chapter can also be calculated on the basis of the Scopus database of Elsevier.

Because the h-index does not take into account the often large differences in citation density between, and even within fields of science, this indicator is in many situations not appropriate for the assessment of research performance. Furthermore, it was recently proved that the h-index is mathematically inconsistent [3].

JIF: I define this indicator with an example: the JIF of a journal for the year 2010 is the number of citations received in 2010 for publications of 2008 and 2009 in this journal, divided by the total number of publications of 2008 and 2009 of the journal. Often, the JIF values are used to weight publications, as a 'proxy' for the real number of citations received by these publications. This is not a good practice as (i) the JIF values are based on a too short citation window (2 years); (ii) JIF values are strongly influenced by the review papers in a journal; reviews are mostly higher cited than 'normal' publications and thus it is important to correct for article type (such as in the indicators *cd/cj, cd/cf, cj/cf*); and (iii) there are inconsistencies and errors in the calculations [4,5]. The JIF values for all journals covered by the WoS can be found in the Journal Citation Reports (JCR®), a separate database of Thomson Reuters. If a university has a subscription to the WoS, the JCR® database is included in this subscription.

References

1. Waltman, L., Calero-Medina, C., Kosten, J. et al. (2012) The Leiden Ranking 2011/2012: data collection, indicators, and interpretation. *Journal of the American Society for Information Science and Technology* **63**, 2419–2432. Open access pre-print version: http://arxiv.org/abs/1202.3941. See more at: http://www.leidenranking.com/methodology/indicators
2. Hirsch, J.E. (2005) An index to quantify an individual's scientific research output. *Proceedings of the National Academy of Sciences of the United States of America* **102**, 16569–16572. Open access pre-print version: http://arxiv.org/abs/physics/0508025
3. Waltman, L. and van Eck, N.J. (2012) The inconsistency of the h-index. *Journal of the American Society for Information Science and Technology* **63**, 406–415. Open access pre-print version: http://arxiv.org/abs/1108.3901
4. Moed, H.F. and van Leeuwen, T.N. (1996) Impact factors can mislead. *Nature* **381**, 186
5. van Leeuwen, T.N. (2012) Discussing some basic critique on journal impact factors: revision of earlier comments. *Scientometrics* **92**, 443–455

Measuring research impact: not everything that can be counted counts, and not everything that counts can be counted

Jane Grimson[1]

School of Computer Science and Statistics, Trinity College Dublin,
The University of Dublin, Ireland

Introduction

Virtually every sector of society and the economy across the world is subject to ongoing monitoring and assessment through an increasingly complex and bewildering array of measurements, metrics and key performance indicators. All of this is being carried out in the name of openness, transparency and account-ability. These performance indicators are being used internationally to benchmark countries against each other, nationally to inform government policy and locally to improve performance within an organization, from increasing shareholder value in a company, to reducing waiting times for elective surgery in a hospital. Even the Millennium Development Goals have given rise to a whole new industry in M&E (Monitoring and Evaluation) of the effectiveness of international aid.

The world of research is no different, and international rankings, citations and impact factors have an increasingly important influence on deciding where investment should be made, whether someone should be promoted and even whether or not they are eligible to apply for a grant.

Although measurements of research quality (bibliometrics) have been around for over 100 years, it is really only in recent years that they have begun to play such an important role in academic life. However, virtually everyone agrees that even the most sophisticated measurement is, at best, a poor proxy for evaluating the richness and the diversity of research and of its social and economic impact. New tools, enabled by web technologies, which are emerging together with the older more traditional citation and impact counts, may offer more comprehensive approaches which are less open to unintended consequences, gaming and perverse incentives.

This chapter does not attempt to conduct an exhaustive study of the issues surrounding the use of bibliometrics as a tool (or set of tools) for the measurement of research quality; rather, it draws parallels with the field of healthcare quality and investigates whether there are any lessons to be learnt which could improve our approach to assessing research quality.

[1]Email: jane.grimson@tcd.ie

Transparency, accountability and trust

Where public expenditure is concerned, the demands for transparency and accountability have increased dramatically in recent years [1] and have been given a further impetus in the current economic climate of cut-backs and austerity. No sector is immune. For the research sector of higher education, the impact has been dramatic with a growing number of articles with catchy titles such as *Users, narcissism and control - tracking the impact of scholarly publications in the 21st Century* [2], *Bibliometrics as weapons of mass citation* [3] and *The follies of citation indices and academic ranking lists* [4]. Although much that has been published has been well researched and evidence-based, and makes recommendations for improved methods of assessing research quality, others simply restrict themselves to a detailed analysis of the inappropriateness of the metrics proposed without putting forward any alternatives, with the remainder representing what could be loosely described as a polemic against such measurement in the name of academic autonomy and independence. That is not to say that academic autonomy and independence are not important; indeed, there are far too many lessons to be learnt from history where their loss has had devastating results for human rights and society as a whole. However, the challenge, as Michael Power puts it, is "balancing the aspiration for autonomy with external pressures for accountability" ([5], p. 2). Power asks whether auditing mechanisms of control (and bibliometrics are essentially a method of auditing the quality of research and ultimately, therefore, of control) are themselves out of control ([5], p. 30) and argues that the burden and cost of the procedures and processes surrounding auditing for both those being audited and the auditors need to be reduced, whereas on the other hand, there needs to be a "rehabilitation of trust" ([5], p. 40).

The issue of trust and the need for a return to it was a major theme of Onora O'Neill's Reith Lectures in 2002 [6]. O'Neill concluded that, "some of the regimes of accountability and transparency developed over the last 15 years may damage rather than reinforce trustworthiness". Similarly, Power concluded that the "technologies of audit may paradoxically achieve the opposite of their intended effect" ([5], p. 27). Commenting on the situation in universities, O'Neill described the forms of accountability to which universities are subjected as "a clumsy attempt to achieve accountability for the greatly increased public revenues supporting teaching and research while maintaining respect for academic freedom and university autonomy" [7].

Measuring healthcare quality

Given this widespread enthusiasm for indicators and performance measurement in general, it is interesting to examine what, if anything, can be learnt from other sectors which might be usefully applied in attempts to measure research quality. Healthcare quality has been a focus of interest and debate within the health sector from the time of Hippocrates, if not before [8]. Today, most researchers and practitioners agree that healthcare quality has six key dimensions, safe, effective, patient-centred, timely, efficient and equitable [9], and all need to be considered in any attempt at assessment. This led to the development of a variety of metrics or KPIs (Key Performance Indicators). There is a growing body of evidence concerning what makes a 'good' KPI, as shown in Table 1 [10].

Indicators should measure what they are supposed to measure (validity); they should give the same answer if measured by different people (reliability); they should be able to measure small changes (sensitivity); they should measure actual changes (specificity); and they should be underpinned by research (evidence-based) [10].

Today, there are a bewildering array of KPIs which are used in health-care, many of which are reported internationally for comparison purposes to the World Health Organization and the Organisation for Economic Co-operation and Development. Not surprisingly, as with research indicators and metrics, much has been written about the benefits and risks associated with their use. On the positive side, unless healthcare providers evaluate or measure what they are doing and how, how can they be confident that they are delivering a safe and high-quality service? And everyone agrees that there must be both quantitative and qualitative measurements to give a balanced picture across all six dimensions of quality. On the negative side, however, there is extensive evidence of 'gaming', concerns over data quality, and an over-reliance on targets and indicators leading to unsafe services [11]. One example of 'gaming' which has been identified in a number of countries concerns waiting times in Emergency Departments. In England, for example, a maximum waiting time target of 4 hours for 95% of patients was introduced in 2004, but when hospitals realized that they were going to miss the target, they refused to accept the patients from the ambulances as the clock did not start until the patient was registered in the Department [12]. In order to counteract this, the National Health Service had to start measuring ambulance turnaround times!

It is also the case that some indicators which are widely used interna-tionally have subsequently turned out to be flawed, and yet they continue to be used. An example is the HSMR (Hospital Standardised Mortality Ratio) which is intended to measure, appropriately risk-adjusted, whether a particular hospital has an unusually high mortality rate. It is used as a proxy for the safety of services provided by that hospital. On the face of it, this seems a reasonable measure, and patients have a right to know whether they are at risk. However, following

Table 1
Criteria for a good KPI

KPI attribute	Meaning
Validity	Does the KPI measure what it is supposed to measure?
Reliability	Does the KPI provide a consistent measure, i.e. does it give the same answer if measured by different people?
Sensitivity	Can the KPI measure small changes?
Specificity	Can the KPI measure actual changes?
Evidence-based	Is the KPI supported by scientific evidence or the consensus of experts?

systematic reviews of the evidence, a number of researchers have shown that the HSMR is an unreliable measure of the quality of care [13,14]. Thomas and Hofer [14] concluded that the calculation of HSMRs is subject to both systematic and random errors. Pitches et al. [13] pointed out that, as approximately 98% of all patients survive their hospital stay, the HSMR is based on only 2% of the population, and it would not be unreasonable to assume that most of the deaths which did occur were unavoidable and not the result of poor care. Through a series of simulations, they showed that the HSMR is a reliable measure of quality of care only if a minimum of 15% of deaths were unavoidable; any less than that will not be picked up by the HSMR. They concluded that even though it is widely used in a number of countries, the HSMR is simply a bad indicator [15] with poor sensitivity and specificity [16].

Thus in spite of many decades of the use of measurement and metrics in healthcare, there are still concerns as to whether they do differentiate between good and poor quality care. They can certainly measure activity levels, waiting times and so on, but actual health outcomes are much more difficult to measure, even in situations where the outcome is apparently as definitive and measurable as death. Furthermore, where funding decisions and league tables are based on these indicators, "the evidence reveals how the system rewards providers not for preventing adverse events or ill health, but for treating patients, even if the illness is caused by the service itself" [17].

Implications for measuring research quality

So what, if anything, can be learnt from the healthcare domain which might ensure that the measurement and metrics used to assess research quality are more robust? Is it possible to come up with a set of indicators that really do differentiate good-quality research from poor-quality research, that will not be subject to gaming and that will not distort practice? And our first problem is to define research quality, and to date, there does not seem to be a consensus [18]. Is research quality the same as research excellence? Where does impact fit in? The Impact of Social Sciences Project at the LSE (London School of Economics) divided research impacts into 'academic impacts', which are instances when research influences actors in academia or universities and 'external impacts', or instances when research influences other actors outside of academia including business, government and civil society [19]. Academic impacts are traditionally measured through bibliometrics, whereas external impacts are measured in a whole variety of different ways ranging from, for example, coverage in the media, to policy influences, patents and spin-off companies. The key question which all of those involved in the evaluation of research personally, institutionally, nationally and internationally seeks to answer is: "What is the scientific and social impact of an individual's research?" ([2], p. 5). The equivalent question in healthcare is: "What is the impact (or outcome) on the individual the health of an individual and/or population at large?" Outcome is regarded as an important aspect of healthcare quality, and therefore it seems reasonable to include impact as part of research quality, rather than regard it as something separate. In healthcare, a broad view of outcome is taken, so a similarly broad view of impact should be taken which encompasses knowledge creation in the sense of increasing our understanding as well as knowledge which is potentially useful socially or economically. In both cases also, it is important to consider both the short- and long-term impacts. The long-term impacts of research can be virtually impossible to track using conventional bibliometrics. For example, Hamilton discovered quaternions in 1843, but it was not until the late 20th Century that they found widespread practical application in computer graphics [20].

Just as in healthcare, there is ample evidence of the potential for gaming of indicators from citation cartels to ghost writers and guest authors (see below). In research, bibliometric indicators, such as citation counts, journal impact factors and publication rates, rely for their validity as measures of research quality on the fact that published research has been subject to peer review [18]. Given the widespread criticisms of peer review, this assumption is not necessary always valid. It would be beyond the scope of this chapter to critique the peer-review system. However, there are three issues which are particularly relevant to the quality debate, namely the inherent conservatism, the problems associated with the identification of plagiarism and fraud, and issues around authorship. There are many examples over the years of the resistance by scientists to scientific discoveries, including those of major figures such as Lister and Maxwell [21], and the House of Commons investigation into peer review in scientific publications identified a "perceived bias towards conservative judgements" or a lack of risk-taking ([22], p. 18). The ultimate "post-publication punishment: retraction", although still quite rare, is increasing [23]. Van Noorden [23] points out that in the 2000s, there were only 30 retraction notices per annum, whereas in 2011 the number of retractions had grown to 400 "even though the total number of papers published has risen by only 44% over the past decade". Perhaps even more alarmingly, retracted papers continue to be cited in the literature with the authors seemingly unaware of the retraction. Fortunately, new approaches are being developed such as CrossMark (http://www.crossref.org/crossmark/), which will draw the reader's attention when downloading a pdf of an article that it has been subsequently retracted or corrected.

Some fraudulent research can have devastating consequences. In 1998, a doctor, Andrew Wakefield, published what subsequently turned out to be a fraudulent paper in *The Lancet* which provided evidence of a link between the combined MMR (measles, mumps and rubella) vaccine and autism ([24], retracted). The findings were widely reported in the media with the result that there was a rapid decline in vaccination uptake which was followed by significantly increased incidence of measles and mumps, resulting in deaths and severe and permanent injuries [25]. The paper was partially retracted in 2003 and fully retracted in 2010. The negative effects are still being felt today.

Authorship has been described as "the main currency in the world of science ... Authorships enable scientists to accumulate citations ... are key to getting grants and winning promotions" [26]. In research generally, but in the biomedical sciences in particular, "authorship provides recognition, but also establishes accountability and responsibility" [27]. Yet, in spite of the central role authorship plays in bibliometrics, it is in fact a poor indicator of the contribution the author has made to the research. Guest authorship, where someone's name is added to a paper even though they have contributed nothing to the intellectual content, research or writing, is not unusual. Equally, ghost authorship, where someone's name is deliberately omitted from the list of authors even though they have made a substantial contribution, has been identified [28]. Both practices are unacceptable. One of the most egregious and widely publicized examples concerned the clinical trial results for the drug rofecoxib (marketed as Vioxx). Rofecoxib is a non-steroidal anti-inflammatory drug used to treat acute and chronic pain. It was very widely prescribed (an estimated 80 million users worldwide), but Merck voluntarily withdrew it from the market in 2004 after disclosures that the company had withheld information for over 5 years about increased risks of heart attack and stroke associated with long-term use of the drug [29]. It was one of the most widely used drugs ever to be withdrawn from the market. The original papers were ghost-written by sponsor employees, but first authorship was attributed to academics who did not always disclose that they had received financial support from Merck [27].

Gender and research quality

In healthcare, ensuring equality of access to treatment is an important dimension of quality; this raises the equivalent question in research, namely whether all researchers have an equal opportunity to contribute to high-quality research and 'maximize their bibliometric score'. Not all disciplines, geographical regions and languages are covered in the same way [30,31]. Consideration has also been given as to whether or not bibliometrics are gender-neutral [32,33]. Certainly by virtue of the fact that the bibliometrics favour the sciences and women are more likely to work in the humanities, they are at a disadvantage relative to their male colleagues in science. However, this bias is due to differences between disciplines and not gender. Bibliometrics rely for their validity on peer review and "the issue of gender and peer review is highly contested" leading to often contradictory conclusions [30]. The first evidence that the peer-review system might not be gender-neutral was a study carried out by two Swedish researchers, Wenneras and Wold [34]. They examined the award of postdoctoral fellowships by the Swedish Research Council and showed that women had to publish 2.6 times as much as men to receive the same score. Although there has been subsequent criticism of their methodology [35], it did lead to most research funders tightening up their review procedures [32]. Even if we accept that the peer-review system is largely gender-neutral, there is irrefutable evidence of unequal participation of men and women in academia which, in turn, damages research quality. "Universities and research institutes are regarded as liberal, meritocratic institutions united in a commitment to academic excellence" [32]. Yet, the "political arithmetic of gender in the academy" tells a different story.

The latest figures published by the European Commission and reproduced in Figure 1 show that although women constitute the majority at undergraduate level (55%), their numbers decrease rapidly, with women comprising just 11% of full professors. Even in fields which have always had larger female partici-

Figure 1

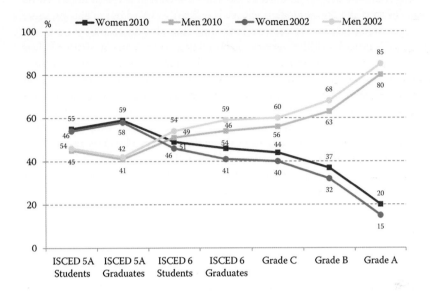

Proportion of men and women in a typical academic career, students and academic staff, EU-27, 2002–2010

ISCE, International Standard Classification of Education. Figure reproduced from [36].

pation, the numbers show that the glass ceiling in academia is still in place, with 28.4% of full professors in the humanities and 19.4% in the social sciences [36]. The numbers in the traditionally male disciplines of engineering and technology are much lower at just 7.9%. Importantly, the report concludes that "there is no evidence of spontaneous reduction of gender inequality over time". A study by Swedish researchers of the differences in career trajectories of men and women with particular reference to achieving full professorships confirms this, concluding: "Measured as chances of advancing to the position of full professors, the career prospects for female university researchers are as bleak today as they were twenty years ago, despite policy programs aimed at promoting female professors" [37]. If one assumes that the ability to conduct good-quality research is equally distributed between the genders, this 'leaky pipeline' where women are lost disproportionally along the career ladder has major implications for research quality. A study by Valian [38] argued that "men and women are socialized into operating with implicit assumptions about gender differences" which result in men being over-rated and women under-rated, by both women and men. More generally, Merton concluded that the contribution of established researchers are consistently given more credit than is due, referred to as the 'Matthew effect' (to those who have more shall be given) [39]. From a gender perspective, this is not so much discrimination against women researchers, but rather the effect of a male bonus.

Research is fundamentally concerned with the quest for new knowledge and understanding or, as the English chemist William Henry (1775–1836) put it, research is "a blind date with knowledge". Research is thus a highly creative endeavour, and "since modern science is primarily carried out in groups, success depends not just on the creative individuals but also on creative groups" [33]. There is extensive evidence from the business world that gender-balanced teams are more innovative and creative [40] and that organizations with women in leadership positions perform better that those run just by men [41]. "Gender balance yields creativity. Focusing on scientific quality ... entails focusing on gender equity" [33].

There is another aspect of gender and research which has received increasing attention in recent years, namely the role of gender in the research itself, the type of research questions being asked and how the research is conducted [42]. Research that is gender blind can also simply be bad research [33]. Men and women are equally represented among society and therefore one would expect, for example, that trials of drugs would consider their effects on both men and women. Heart disease manifests differently in men and women yet the majority of studies have been performed on men with the result that women are often mis- or under-diagnosed ([42], p. 22). Equally, research on osteoporosis-related hip fractures was based on women with the result that men (who account for one-third of the total) are rarely evaluated or appropriately treated [43]. Climate-change research is generally scientifically and technically driven and therefore largely a male-dominated area. Yet, according to the Food and Agricultural Organization of the United Nations, women account for 60–80% of rural farmers and produce nearly 90% of the food on the continent [44]. They are therefore the ones most immediately affected by climate change and need to be actively involved in the development of appropriate solutions and approaches in setting the research agenda. At a recent conference on Hunger, Food and Climate Justice, Etrida Luhanga, a rural farmer from Malawi, pointed out that often the people who were sitting around the table deciding how best to adapt or mitigate the effects of climate change know nothing about farming and are only there "because they can read and write". She argued strongly for the inclusion of rural farmers and women in particular who are experiencing the effects of climate change on a daily basis in the development of effective solutions [45].

Conclusions

This paper has examined traditional bibliometrics as a method of measuring research quality through the lens of the use of KPIs to measure healthcare quality. It is widely recognized in both fields that the use of such metrics can be associated with gaming, perverse incentives and distortions of practice, thus undermining their validity. There are many ways in which the current set of bibliometrics could be improved which would help to reduce the inbuilt biases and distortions and the potential for gaming. Although it is possible to eliminate self-citation, citation cartels will inevitably be more difficult to identify since those working in a given field of research will inevitably cite the work of others in the same field. Further investigation would be required in order to be sure that the citation was actually of direct relevance to the particular paper. Clear and verifiable rules around authorship would be highly desirable. But as Biagioli [46] concludes: "rather than pursue the chimera of the one conceptually 'right' definition, one may take a more pragmatic position by acknowledging that authorships (scientific or not) has always been a matter of compromises and negotiations, and that no new conditions have emerged to change that".

Web 2.0 technologies including social networks have generated a myriad of methods for tracking and commenting on research in what Van Noorden [47] described as "a Cambrian explosion of metrics". Wouters and Costas [2] identified and analysed 16 different tools and concluded that there was a need for a concerted research effort into understanding "the dynamics, properties, and potential use of new web based metrics" and how they relate to established indicators in the hope that this "may contribute to the development of more useful tools for the scientific and scholarly community" ([2], p. 45). In particular, they might provide evidence of impact, of "how new research findings are being read, cited, used and transformed in practical results and applications" ([2], p. 5). Bollen et al. [48] conducted a detailed study of new impact measures and concluded that "scientific impact is a multi-dimensional construct that cannot be adequately measured by one single factor".

In healthcare, there is widespread recognition that indicators are just that, simply a proxy indication of quality, and that in order to truly understand whether the care being provided is safe and of good quality, it is necessary to consider many other, generally qualitative, issues. The risk of data-driven, as opposed to evidence-driven, indicators is widely recognized in healthcare [49], and similar problems have been identified with bibliometrics. Just because it is possible to measure an increasingly large number of aspects of research, does not necessarily mean that the results provide a better or more accurate measure of research quality ([47], p. 1). It seems that, to some extent, it is traditional bibliometrics which define what constitutes research quality rather than providing objective measures of research quality. Furthermore, they do not fully measure up to the requirements of validity, reliability, sensitivity, specificity, and underpinned by evidence, which should characterize a good indicator [10]. There needs to be the same recognition, particularly when assessing the performance of the individual researcher, that bibliometrics measure, however imperfectly, only some of the dimensions of research quality and that there is no substitute for a detailed study of the researcher's output.

But the biggest concern in both research and healthcare is the potential to distort practice or 'what gets measured gets done'. And there is plenty of evidence of this from the healthcare domain. The recent public enquiry into events at Mid-Staffordshire NHS Foundation Trust concluded that the failures which resulted in the deaths of 400–1200 patients over a 4-year period from 2005 were, in part, a consequence of "…allowing a focus on reaching national access targets, achieving financial balance and seeking foundation trust status … at the cost of delivering acceptable standards of care" [50]. In research, there are many ways in which bibliometrics can distort practice, from discouraging risk-taking to focusing on research that is likely to be published rather than on research that will provide evidence to influence policy for the benefit of society. This is particularly evident in the context of international development research which seeks to address major global challenges [31]. The challenge is that in attempting to measure the quality of healthcare and of research, the ultimate and definitive assessment can only be made in the long term with the benefit of hindsight. Medical treatment is given on the basis of the best available knowledge at that time, which may subsequently prove to be wrong, but this does not necessarily reflect negatively on the quality of the original research. In research, Tim Berners-Lee posted links to the computer code for the World Wide Web which in 1991 he had developed on the alt.hypertext discussion group so others could download it and play with it. No one at that time predicted the dramatic impact this invention was to have on all aspects of society across the world a decade later. It is only in the long term that we can really understand whether or not a health intervention has been beneficial or whether a particular piece of research is truly groundbreaking.

In addition to the problem of hindsight, there are other aspects of research quality which are not currently measured, either because they have not been considered as a dimension of research quality or because they are inherently difficult to measure. The OA (open access) movement is one such example. OA is concerned with making scholarly peer-reviewed publications freely available on the Internet [51,52]. The increase in the adoption of OA publication mandates represents an important development in making research results more widely available while at the same time benefiting the researchers through increased citation rates. Making a publication openly available should be reflected in the assessment of research quality. But arguably it is the open-data movement which may have greater implications for the assessment of research quality. Open data is the idea that certain data should be freely available to everyone to use and republish as they wish, without restrictions [53,54]. Providing OA to research results and data potentially speeds up the process of knowledge discovery, and therefore there is an argument to be made for including it as part of a suite of research quality indicators. The benefits of OA to research data was clearly demonstrated by the now infamous paper by Reinhart and Rogoff [55] which had a major impact on global economic policy and which was subsequently shown by Herndon, Ash and Pollin [56] to have been based on an incorrect Excel spreadsheet. The errors in the spreadsheet were such as to invalidate the conclusions of the paper, but not in time to prevent the results of the original paper contributing to widespread adoption of programmes of austerity in many countries.

Finally, existing approaches to the measurement of research quality are largely gender blind; yet, there is ample evidence to show that gender plays an important role in research quality, in terms of setting the research agenda, but also in ensuring that the 'system' supports the best researchers to do the best research. Good male researchers have nothing to fear from the inclusion of gender as a dimension of research quality!

So in summary, conventional bibliometrics give, at best, only a partial indication of research quality. As Wouters and Costas [2] have recommended, there is a need for much more research into the validity and impact of them and of the new web-based metrics. But, above all, there is a need to agree, first, on what exactly constitutes high-quality research, and secondly, whether and how it might be effectively measured.

References

1. Engwall, L. and Scott, P. (2013) Setting the scene. In *Wenner-Gren International Series Volume 86: Trust in Universities* (Engwall, L. and Scott, P., eds), pp. 1–13, Portland Press Ltd, London

2. Wouters, P. and Costas, R. (2012) Users, narcissism and control – tracking the impact of scholarly publications in the 21st Century. SURF Foundation, Utrecht, The Netherlands. http://research-acumen.eu/wp-content/uploads/Users-narcissism-and-control.pdf (Accessed 21 February 2013)

3. Molinié, A. and Bodenhausen, G. (2010) Bibliometrics as weapons of mass citation. *Chimia* **64**, 78–89

4. Ernst, R. (2010) The follies of citation indices and academic ranking lists: a brief commentary to 'bibliometrics as weapons of mass citation'. *Chimia* **64**, 90

5. Power, M. (1996) *The Audit Explosion*. DEMOS, London. http://www.demos.co.uk/files/theauditexplosion.pdf (Accessed 21 February 2013)

6. O'Neill, O. (2002) A question of trust. BBC Radio 4 Reith Lectures 2002. http://www.bbc.co.uk/radio4/reith2002/ (Accessed 21 February 2013)

7. O'Neill, O. (2012) Integrity and quality in universities: accountability, excellence and success. *British Academy Review* **20**, 41–43

8. Merry, M.D. and Crago, M.G. (2001) The past, present and future of healthcare quality. *Physician Executive* **5**, 30–35

9. Institute of Medicine (2001) *Crossing The Quality Chasm: A New Health System For The 21st Century*. National Academy Press, Washington DC

10. Health Information and Quality Authority (2013) *Guidance on Developing Key Performance Indicators (KPIs) and Minimum Data Sets*. http://www.hiqa.ie/publications/guidance-developing-key-performance-indicators-kpis-and-minimum-data-sets-monitor-healt (Accessed 3 May 2013)

11. Bowen, S. and Kreindler, S.A. (2008) Indicator madness: a cautionary reflection on the use of indicators in healthcare. *Healthcare Policy* **4**, 41–48

12. Campbell, D. (2008) Scandal of patients left for hours outside A&E. In *The Observer*. Sunday 17 February 2008, http://www.guardian.co.uk/society/2008/feb/17/health.nhs1 (Accessed 4 May 2013)

13. Pitches, D.W., Mohammed, M.A. and Lilford, R.J. (2007) What is the empirical evidence that hospitals with higher-risk adjusted mortality rates provide poorer quality care? A systematic review of the literature. *BMC Health Services Research* **7**, 91

14. Thomas, J.W. and Hofer, T.P. (1998) Research evidence in the validity of risk-adjusted mortality rate as a measure of hospital quality of care. *Medical Care Research and Review* **55**, 371–404

15. Taylor, P. (2013) Rigging the death rate. *London Review of Books* **35**, 12–15

16. Scott, I., Brand, C., Phelps, G., Barker, A. and Cameron, P. (2011) Using hospital standardised mortality ratios to assess quality of care: proceed with extreme caution. *Medical Journal of Australia* **194**, 645–648

17. Øvretveit, J. (2009) *Does Improving Quality Save Money?* The Health Foundation, London. http://www.health.org.uk/publications/does-improving-quality-save-money/ (Accessed 12 May 2013)

18. Méndez, E. (2012) *Evaluating Research Excellence: Main Debates*. International Development Research Centre, Ottawa. http://www.idrc.ca/EN/Documents/Brief-Final-English.pdf (Accessed 4 May 2013)

19. LSE Public Policy Group (2011) *Maximizing the Impacts of Your Research: A Handbook for Social Scientists*. London School of Economics, London. http://eprints.lse.ac.uk/35758/1/Handbook_PDF_for_the_LSE_impact_blog_April_2011.pdf (Accessed 4 May 2013)

20. Shoemake, K. (1985) Animating rotations with quaternion curves. *Computer Graphics* **19**, 245–254

21. Barber, B. (1961) Resistance by scientists to scientific discovery. *Science* **134**, 596–602

22. House of Commons Science and Technology Committee (2011) Peer review in scientific publications. http://www.publications.parliament.uk/pa/cm201012/cmselect/cmsctech/856/856.pdf (Accessed 5 May 2013)

23. Van Noorden, R. (2011) The trouble with retractions. *Nature* **478**, 26–28

24. Wakefield, A., Murch, S., Anthony, A. et al. (1998) Ileal-lymphoid-nodular hyperplasia, non-specific colitis, and pervasive developmental disorder in children. *Lancet* **351**, 637–641 (Retrieved 5 September 2007); retraction **375**, 445 (2010)

25. Pepys, M.B. (2007) Science and serendipity. *Clinical Medicine* **7**, 562–578

26. Frische, S. (2012) It is time for full disclosure of author contributions. *Nature* **489**, 475

27. Ross, J.S., Hill, K.P., Egilman, D.S. and Krumholz, H.M. (2008) Guest authorship and ghostwriting in publications related to rofecoxib. *Journal of the American Medical Association* **299**, 1800–1812

28. Stemwedel, J.D. (2011) Scientific authorship: guests, courtesy, contributions, and harms. In *Scientific American*. 4 November 2011, http://blogs.scientificamerican.com/doing-good-science/2011/11/04/scientific-authorship-guests-courtesy-contributions-and-harms/ (Accessed 5 May 2013)

29. Knox, R. (2004) Merck pulls arthritis drug Vioxx from market. http://www.npr.org/templates/story/story.php?storyId=4054991

30. Coryn, C.L. (2005) The use and abuse of citations as indicators of research quality. *Journal of MultiDisciplinary Evaluation* **4**, 115–121

31. Tijssen, R.J., Mouton, J., van Leeuwen, T.N. and Boshoff, N. (2006) How relevant are local scholarly journals in global science? A case study of South Africa. *Research Evaluation* **15**, 163–174

32. Rees, T. (2011) The gendered construction of scientific excellence. *Interdisciplinary Science Reviews* **36**, 133–145

33. Rice, C. (2011) Scientific (E)quality. *Interdisciplinary Science Reviews* **36**, 114–124

34. Wenneras, C. and Wold, A. (1997) Nepotism and sexism in peer review. *Nature* **347**, 341–343

35. Mutz, R., Bornmann, L. and Daniel, H.-D. (2012) Does gender matter in grant peer review? An empirical investigation using the example of the Austrian Science Fund. *Zeitschrift für Psychologie* **220**, 121–129

36. European Commission (2012) She figures 2012: gender in research and innovation. Directorate-General for Research and Innovation. http://ec.europa.eu/research/science-society/document_library/pdf_06/she-figures-2012_en.pdf (Accessed 4 May 2013)

37. Danell, R. and Hjern, M. (2012) Career Prospects for Female University Researchers: Event History Analysis of Career Trajectories at Swedish Universities. Proceedings of 17th International Conference on Science and Technology Indicators (Archambault, E., Gingras, Y. and Larivière, V., eds), 228–235, Science-Metrix and OST, Montréal

38. Valian, V. (1999) *Why So Slow? The Advancement of Women*. MIT Press, Cambridge, MA

39. Merton, R.K. (1968) The Matthew effect in science. *Science* **159**, 56–63

40. London Business School (2007) Innovative potential: men and women in teams. http://www.london.edu/assets/documents/facultyandresearch/Innovative_Potential_NOV_2007.pdf (Accessed 5 May 2013)

41. McKinsey & Company (2010) Women Matter 3: women leaders, a competitive edge in and after the crisis. http://www.mckinsey.de/downloads/publikation/women_matter/women_matter_3_brochure.pdf (Accessed 12 May 2013)

42. European Commission (2012) Structural change in research institutions: enhancing excellence, gender equality and efficiency in research and innovation. Directorate-General for Research and Innovation. http://ec.europa.eu/research/science-society/document_library/pdf_06/structural-changes-final-report_en.pdf (Accessed 5 May 2013)

43. Schiebinger, L., Klinge, I., Sánchez de Madariaga, I., Schraudner, M. and Stefanick, M. (eds.) (2011–2013) Gendered Innovations in Science, Health & Medicine, Engineering and Environment. Osteoporosis research in men: rethinking standards and reference models. http://genderedinnovations.stanford.edu/case-studies/osteoporosis.html

44. Food and Agricultural Organisation (2013) Women, agriculture and rural development: a synthesis report of the Africa region. http://www.fao.org/docrep/X0250E/X0250E00.htm (Accessed 5 May 2013)

45. Luhanga, E. (2013) Thanks from Grassroots. Conference on Hunger, Nutrition and Climate Justice, Dublin Castle, 15–16 April 2013. http://www.youtube.com/watch?v=KaWIsoadrFQ&feature=youtube_gdata_player (Accessed 4 May 2013)

46. Biagioli, M. (1998) The instability of authorship: credit and responsibility in contemporary biomedicine. *The FASEB Journal* **12**, 3–16

47. Van Noorden, R. (2010) A profusion of measures. *Nature* **465**, 864–866

48. Bollen, J., Van de Sompel, H., Hagberg, A. and Chute, R. (2009) A principal component analysis of 39 scientific impact measures. *PLoS ONE* **4**, e6022

49. Bowen, S., Erickson, T., Martens, P. and Crockett, S. (2009) More than "using research": the real challenges in promoting evidence-informed decision-making. *Healthcare Policy* **4**, 87–102

50. Francis, R. (2013) Report of the Mid-Staffordshire NHS Foundation Trust Public Inquiry. http://www.midstaffspublicinquiry.com/report (Accessed 5 May 2013)

51.   European Research Advisory Board (2006) Scientific Publication: Policy on Open Access. Final report. http://ec.europa.eu/research/eurab/pdf/eurab_scipub_report_recomm_dec06_en.pdf (Accessed 6 May 2013)

52.   Houghton, J. and Sheehan, P. (2006) The economic impact of enhanced access to research findings. CSES Working Paper No. 23, July 2006. Centre for Strategic Economic Studies, Victoria University, Melbourne. http://www.cfses.com/documents/wp23.pdf (Accessed 11 August 2013)

53.   Auer, S.R., Bizer, C., Kobilarov, G., Lehmann, J., Cyganiak, R. and Ives Z. (2007) DBpedia: A Nucleus for a Web of Open Data. The Semantic Web. Proceedings of 6th International Semantic Web Conference, 2nd Asian Semantic Web Conference, ISWC 2007 + ASWC 2007, Busan, Korea, 11–15 November 2007 (Aberer, K., Choi, K.-S., Noy, N. et al. eds.), 722–735, Springer, Lecture Notes in Computer Science 4825

54.   Open Data Institute. What is open data? http://theodi.org/guides/what-open-data

55.   Reinhart, C.M. and Rogoff, K.S. (2010) Growth in a time of debt. *American Economic Review* 100, 573–578

56.   Herndon, T., Ash, M., and Pollin, R. (2013) Does high public debt consistently stifle economic growth? A critique of Renhart and Rogoff. Political Economy Research Institute, University of Massachusetts Amherst, Working Paper Series No. 322. http://www.peri.umass.edu/fileadmin/pdf/working_papers/working_papers_301-350/WP322.pdf (Accessed 11 August 2013)

PART III: INDICATORS FOR RANKINGS

5

Scientific performance indicators: a critical appraisal and a country-by-country analysis

Michel Gevers[1]

Department of Mathematical Engineering, ICTEAM, Université catholique de Louvain, Belgium

Introduction

The evaluation culture has invaded the university environment over the last 20 years. University administrators have often adopted standard 'business models' based on competition and comparison, as if university education and research was to be treated with the same rules and criteria as any private company on the market. Students are described more and more as customers, and universities compete to attract academics that have the best potential to increase their position in the international rankings. Academics and administrators of universities, and research funding agencies, spend more and more time performing evaluation and selection, and they want tools that simplify their tasks. As a result, a whole new research area has opened up for the production of performance indicators at all levels of these evaluation procedures.

In the scientific world, performance is evaluated and comparisons are made at essentially four different levels: the individual researcher, the scientific journal, the university or research organization, and the country. At each of these levels, performance indicators have been produced that are supposed to evaluate quality, with a view to facilitating the tasks of the overburdened evaluators. A frantic search is going on at these different levels for the design of a single number that would characterize quality. These indicators are continuously being revised, refined and improved. 'Any number beats no number' seems to be the new motto. The availability of these indicators is leading to an oversimplification of the quality assessments that are performed at these different levels. In addition, the emergence of every new indicator brings with it the development of feedback strategies whereby the researchers, the journals, the institutions and the countries aim at increasing their relative position as reflected by the indicator rather than pursuing sound and long-term research strategies.

In the first part of this chapter, I examine the leading indicators that are presently used at these four evaluation levels and illustrate some of the obnoxious feedback strategies that they have generated and their consequences. I then attempt to describe what the qualities of a good performance indicator are, and spell out a

[1]Email: michel.gevers@uclouvain.be

number of precautions and recommendations that should be adopted when using these indicators.

In the second part of this chapter, I perform a comparative analysis of the scientific performance of 17 countries that are known to be very active in research, where the performance is measured by citations. In order to compare countries that have vastly different populations and financial means, I introduce three different normalizations. The first consists of computing the number of citations per document. The second relates the number of citations to the budget invested by each country in fundamental research, and the third is based on a so-called NI (Normalized Impact) that takes account of the size of the institutions, the discipline and the time period.

The four levels of performance evaluation

Scientific performance is evaluated at essentially four different levels: the researcher, the scientific journal, the university or research organization, and the country. In the present chapter, I briefly present these four levels of performance evaluation, and the most prevalent performance indicators that have been introduced at these levels. In the next section, I describe the feedback effects that these indicators have induced in the scientific community, and the uses and abuses of these indicators.

The researcher is evaluated first and foremost at the various steps of his/her scientific career: at the hiring stage for a post-doc or academic position, at the promotion stage to a higher grade or position, and at the application for a grant or for a scientific prize. Whereas in the old days most researchers tended to accomplish their career at the place where they first obtained a tenured position, nowadays an ever-growing proportion of the academic community tends to shift allegiances and to move along to positions considered to be more rewarding or more prestigious. In this pursuit for 'excellence', the market value of the researcher becomes the key ingredient. At present, this market value is essentially assessed by the number of publications, the 'quality' of the journals in which these papers are published, and the impact of the publications as measured by the number of citations. To facilitate the task of the assessors, some indicators have been devised that are supposed to aggregate with just one number the research output and performance of the candidate. The most famous of these indicators is the Hirsch index [1], best known as the h-index. A researcher has an h-index of 20, say, if 20 of his/her publications have been cited at least 20 times.

The enormous pressure to 'publish or perish' has led to an explosion of the number of published papers together with an explosion of the number of journals, of widely varying quality. The competition between the journals has become fierce, and the need has arisen to try and evaluate the 'quality' of these journals. This has led to the creation of the infamous 'journal impact factor'. It has also led some large research organizations to propose a classification of all journals in different categories. For example, the ARC (Australian Research Council) had proposed a classification of thousands of scientific journals in three categories [2].

This classification was widely used around the world, but after a couple of years and widespread criticism, the ARC abandoned its use [3].

Ever since the publication of the first Shanghai rankings in 2003, the universities have also entered into the game of competition and comparison. A number of competing international rankings have flourished, most of them focusing on research performance with a heavy bias towards natural sciences and medicine, at the expense of humanities and social sciences. The most widely cited rankings nowadays, besides the Shanghai ranking, are those established by the Times Higher Education, Leiden University and U.S. News & World Report, as well as the new U-Multirank whose development is funded by the European Union. One measure of the failure of these rankings to create a consensus about a quality measure for the universities is that they are constantly being revised, making it very difficult to distinguish a trend in the evolution of the performance of any given university.

Finally, a fourth level of performance evaluation has recently made its mark: the comparative analysis of scientific performance of countries, based on aggregates of the performance indicators of their scientific institutions. These comparative analyses are being used by some governments to reorganize their scientific policies, or to reshape the landscape of their scientific institutions. The second part of this chapter will be entirely devoted to such country-by-country performance evaluation.

Engineering the indicators: the feedback effects and their consequences

Every new indicator, at whatever level, brings with it adaptation strategies. As soon as the research community finds out that a particular performance criterion becomes dominant in the evaluation committees, some of its members adapt their research and publication strategy to maximize its impact on the newly adopted criterion rather than aiming at producing the most highly creative research results. This 'feedback effect' can have very negative consequences, to the extent that it may threaten the credibility of the research community and the foundations on which the pursuit of scientific research are established. Even though most of these indicators are very recent (the famous h-index was invented as recently as 2005), their widespread use at all levels of performance evaluation has produced, in a very short time, deleterious effects that are already very visible. In this section, I analyse some of these effects, and their potential long-term consequences on the quality of the produced research and on the undermining of the integrity of the research community.

At the individual researcher level, the focus on publication and citation numbers has resulted in an explosion in the number of papers. Authors, particularly at the early stage of their career, rush to publication. They tend to split their research findings into several papers rather than writing a comprehensive paper, thereby harming the pedagogical quality of their publications. Authors revise their accepted papers even if they realize that in the meantime their results have been superseded by some other researcher. The most important objective for a young researcher is not so much to produce a high-quality paper, but rather to build up a

CV and publication list that will impress their next evaluation committee. But the most deleterious effect of this obsession with indicators is that researchers, whether young or more mature, tend to stay away from long-term or risky research topics for two reasons: long-term projects do not lead to large numbers of papers in a short time, whereas risky and entirely novel topics will typically not be cited widely until years later because the research community in these new topics is still non-existent at the time of publication.

The IF (impact factor) of a journal is based on the number of citations of papers published in that journal over a period of 2 (IF2) or 5 (IF5) years after publication. It is an extraordinarily poor measure of 'quality' for different reasons:

- It measures the instantaneous (or very short-term) impact of a paper, which has very little to do with its quality. Seminal papers are those that have a lasting impact, i.e. that are still being cited 10 or 20 years later.
- The IF of a journal has more to do with the duration of the reviewing process and publication process than with the impact on the research community. If most journals within a scientific discipline take an average of 2 years for the reviewing plus publication process (as can happen in a number of disciplines) then these journals will have an IF2 that is close to zero. Thus it is impossible to compare disciplines that have very different delays for their reviewing and publication processes. One way to increase the IF is to reduce the reviewing time by relaxing the quality criteria, thereby leading to a decrease in the quality of the journal.
- The pressure of the journals to increase their IF eliminates visionary or groundbreaking research because an author who is ahead of his/her time and ventures into virgin territory will typically not be cited until years later.

The use of the IF as a supposed quality criterion for the evaluation of journals is where the manipulation and abuses are taking on the most enormous proportions. To illustrate this, and at the same time, highlight the argument in the last item above, let me cite some recent instructions to authors of a well-established engineering journal, the *IEEE Transactions on Industrial Electronics*:

> *Review criteria: (1) Likelihood for citations of the manuscript.*
> *Our current impact factor is 3.439 and this means that each paper is cited by journal papers at least 5 times within a couple of years after publication. Such expectation is currently the major criterion for review.*

> *FAQ: How many references are needed?*
> *We usually expect a minimum of 20 references, primarily to journal papers. [...] Please be sure that you have current references (last couple of years). If there are no current references, then there are two possibilities:*
>   - *Authors are not following literature*
>   - *There are no papers because other people are not interested in the subject*

> *Both reasons are good enough for manuscript rejection.*

This has led a number of Fellows of the IEEE to send a protest letter to the Board of Directors of the IEEE.

At the level of universities and research organizations, enormous efforts and large budgets are spent by some universities to improve their positions in the world rankings. Engineering the position in the rankings sometimes takes precedence over the pursuit of the university's stated objectives. For example, some universities are hiring prestigious academics for short-term visits at huge fees while requesting them to put the university in their affiliation in all their future publications. Other universities are mandating their newly hired academics, who are on tenure-track positions, to publish at least so many articles in their first 3 years.

The availability and widespread dissemination of international rankings has led some governments to enter into the evaluation frenzy and to reassess their higher-education policy and its organizational structure. In Italy, the Ministry of Higher Education has spent large amounts of money to evaluate each Italian researcher using a combination of indicators and peer-review assessments. Alarmed by the relatively poor position of the French universities and research organizations in the international rankings, the French government has reorganized the university landscape by creating large conglomerates under the belief that size matters, i.e. that large institutions will score higher in the international rankings.

In this brief review of the uses and misuses of research performance indicators, I have argued that the engineering of these indicators at the various levels of evaluation has a significant impact on the type and quality of the research, and on the integrity and credibility of the scientific community. It also has a huge cost in terms of the man-hours invested in the various evaluation procedures and in the manipulation of the indicators.

Qualities of a good performance indicator

Research performance indicators are the subject of intense discussion and activity within the scientific community of experts in bibliometrics and scientometrics, and within a number of international organizations. Specialized journals are devoted to the topic, such as *Scientometrics*, *Research Evaluation* and *Journal of the American Society of Information Science*. International organizations have been set up that are entirely devoted to the topic, such as the IREG (International Ranking Expert Group). They publish policy statements, such as the Berlin Principles on Ranking of Higher Education Institutions [4], established by IREG in May 2006. A more recent initiative is the San Francisco Declaration on Research Assessment, also known as DORA (http://am.ascb.org/dora/), elaborated in December 2012; its main recommendation is that journal-based metrics, such as journal impact factors, should never be used to assess an individual scientist's contributions, or in hiring, promotion or funding decisions.

What are the qualities of a good performance indicator? In the publication by Gingras [5], three criteria have been proposed that are considered as necessary conditions for the validity of an indicator.

- Adequacy of the indicator to the property it is supposed to measure.

The level of investment in Research and Development in a country is a good measure of the intensity of research activity in that country, but it cannot be used as a measure of the quality of the research. Similarly, the number of Nobel prizes received by graduates or academics of a university does not reflect the quality of the education at that university today, because the last Nobel Prize may have been awarded decades ago.

- Sensitivity to the intrinsic inertia of the object.

Universities have a huge inertia; their quality cannot change dramatically in a year. Therefore an *annual* ranking in which a university moves in a single year by five or ten places shows that the indicator is defective, not that the quality of that institution has plummeted or risen dramatically. As argued by Gingras [5], *annual* rankings of universities can therefore only be explained by marketing strategies of the ranking organizations; they serve no scientific purpose, but they absorb a lot of resources from the universities that have to produce the data.

- Homogeneity of the dimensions of the indicator.

A homogeneous indicator of the research output could be the number of papers produced. However, if one combines the number of papers with a citation measure (as is done in the h-index), then one obtains a heterogeneous indicator. The same occurs with indicators that are based on a weighted average of different indicators. Quoting from Gingras [5]: "Combining different indicators into a single number is like transforming a multi dimensional space into a single point, thus losing nearly all the information contained in the different axes".

The following are two additional criteria that should in my view be applied in selecting indicators.

- Insensitivity to small variations in the data: small numbers must be avoided.

A good indicator should not change substantially if one of the input data changes by a small number. For example, one additional Nobel Prize or the death of one Nobel Laureate in a university does clearly not change the quality of this university and should therefore not change its ranking substantially. A corollary is that indicators should not rely on small numbers.

- Normalization with respect to field, time period and size.

It makes no sense to compare research output in different fields or at different periods using the same indicator, because the publication culture varies widely over disciplines and because the level of activity in different topics can change rapidly. In addition, the sizes of the research communities in different disciplines are vastly different. In mathematics, most papers have single authors, whereas in nuclear physics it is not uncommon to have more than 100 authors on a paper. The research community on social networks was very modest 10 years ago, but the field has become enormously popular in the last decade; it makes no sense to compare the h-index of a young post-doc with that of a senior academic. Attempts have been made to address those problems by introducing normalized indices. One such normalized indicator, at the institution level, is the so-called NI, introduced by the Karolinska Institutet in Sweden. It compares the scientific impact, measured by citation numbers, of an institution with the world average in the same scientific domain and over the same period while taking account of the size of that institution.

Research performance of countries, measured by citations

Against the above backdrop, I will now evaluate and compare the research performance of 17 countries that are considered very active in fundamental research, on the basis of the number of citations of papers produced within these countries. The number of citations of a document is indeed one important indicator of the impact of a research paper or book within a discipline. The 17 countries selected in this analysis are Australia, Belgium, Canada, China, Denmark, Finland, France, Germany, Israel, Italy, Japan, The Netherlands, Spain, Sweden, Switzerland, U.K. and U.S.A.

In keeping with the remarks made about the qualities of a performance indicator, I introduce three types of normalizations, which allows comparison of countries of very different sizes and whose domains of excellence may vary widely. Thus for the 17 countries selected for this analysis, I look at the number of citations per document, the number of citations of a country versus the budget invested by that country in fundamental research, and finally the NI as mentioned above.

The analysis was performed using data available from the websites of the World Bank (http://data.worldbank.org), the OECD (Organisation for Economic Cooperation and Development; http://www.oecd-ilibrary.org) and SCImago (http://www.scimagojr.com), a website that is specialized in the ranking of journals and countries on the basis of citations of papers and that is powered by Scopus (http://www.scopus.com), a database of scientific documents and citations maintained by Elsevier. This comparative analysis of the scientific performance of countries was inspired by Giuseppe De Nicolao, a founder of the website ROARS (Return On Academic ReSearch) (http://www.roars.it), whose help is gratefully acknowledged.

The SCImago website allows one to compute citation numbers of documents published in all possible countries over the period 1996–2011, or separately for each year of that period. The number of citations given for a specific country and for a particular year X is the number of citations of all papers published by authors who work at an institution of that country during the year X and cited during the years X, X+1, X+2, etc., up to 2011. Thus, the citation numbers for the year 2009, say, refer to the number of citations of all documents published in 2009 and cited in 2009, 2010 or 2011. When referring to the period 1996–2011, all documents published during that period are considered.

Citations per document

The first normalized data represent the average number of citations per document for the countries involved. Figure 1 shows the ranking of the 17 countries in terms

Figure 1

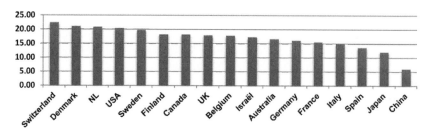

Number of citations per document for the period 1996–2011

of the number of citations per document over the long period (1996–2011). In order to evaluate whether this indicator has evolved over the years, these data have also been computed separately for the years 2010 and 2011. This allows one to check whether the relative positions have evolved over this 15-year period.

Of course, one should bear in mind that the variance for these much shorter periods is significantly larger than for the longer period. Figure 2 shows the country rankings, in terms of citation number per document, for the year 2011.

Figure 3 shows the rankings of the countries for the year 2010. It is much the same as for 2011 (and remember that the variance is lower than for the ranking in 2011): Sweden is in 4th position and Belgium in 5th, whereas Israel is in 10th position after Canada.

In comparing the recent data with those averaged over a 15-year period, it is remarkable to observe that the position of the top three countries has remained unchanged. In addition, Sweden is continuously in the top group. On the other

Figure 2

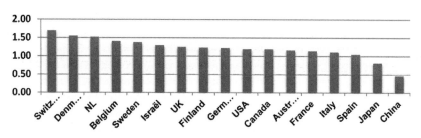

Number of citations per document for the year 2011

Figure 3

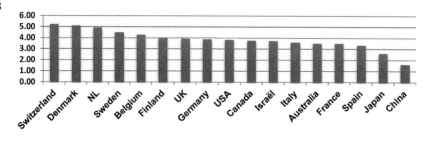

Number of citations per document for the year 2010

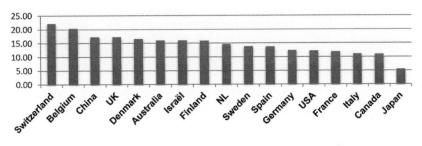

Citation numbers in 2011 against investment in HERD in 2008

hand, Belgium has moved significantly upward while the position of the U.S.A. has declined significantly.

Return on investment: citations versus budget for research

A second way of producing comparisons between countries of different sizes is to examine the return on investment. Given that citation counts are really a measure that reflects the scientific performance of fundamental research (Industrial Research and Development is typically less conducive to publications), I have considered the investments of the 17 countries in Higher Education Research and Development (referred to as HERD by the OECD). In order to evaluate the return on investment, the number of citations produced in 2010 is divided, for each country, by the investment in HERD in 2008, thus allowing for some lag between investment and a measure of its return. The results appear in Figure 4.

To check the robustness of this ranking, I computed the same graphs for the citations in 2010 against HERD in 2008, as well as the citations in 2008 versus HERD in 2006; the relative positions remain essentially unchanged. In particular, Switzerland is always in the top position and Belgium in second, whereas the U.K. is always within the top four.

Comparing countries by NI

The NI has been defined above for the evaluation of a scientific institution. By adding the citation numbers for all institutions of a country, it can also be used to compare countries. Such comparison has been performed by Professor Félix de Moya Anegon, who produced Figure 5, in which the NI was computed for 50 countries, with the world average set at one [6]. Figure 5, produced in 2010, shows that the universities that achieve the highest NI are to be found in the U.K. and the U.S.A., but the latter country has by far the largest spread between high-performing and low-performing universities. Another remarkable feature is the very small spread of the NI between the 'best' and the 'worst' universities in

Figure 5

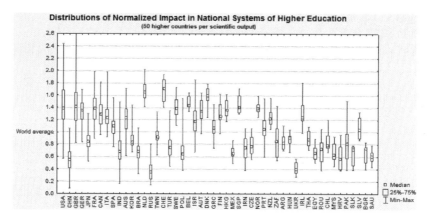

Distributions of Normalized Impact in National Systems of Higher Education
(50 higher countries per scientific output)

NI of Higher Education Institutions in 50 countries

Reproduced from http://www.scimagolab.com/blog/2011/the-research-impact-of-national-higher-education-systems/

Belgium, Norway, Singapore and New Zealand, with a median that is always well above the world average for these countries. Thus a PhD student who decides to go to one of these countries knows that he/she will be in a good place, whatever university he/she chooses within those countries.

Conclusions

I have discussed the most commonly used research performance indicators at the four levels at which evaluations typically take place: the researcher, the journal, the institution and the country. I have argued that the introduction of every new indicator produces the introduction of feedback strategies whose aims are to increase the value of the indicator, sometimes at the expense of the quality of the research and of the research output. These negative effects have been illustrated with examples, at all four levels mentioned above. Nevertheless, indicators are useful provided they are well thought out and used with great care. This has led to the proposal of a number of quality criteria that performance indicators should possess.

In the second part of this chapter, I proposed an evaluation and comparison of the scientific performance of countries as measured by citation counts. In keeping with the quality criteria defined for performance indicators, I have used indicators that are adequately normalized; in addition, my comparative analysis has been based on not just one, but three normalized criteria. One should bear in mind that citation counts are but one of several indicators of research performance. I leave it to each reader to draw his/her own conclusions concerning the scientific performance of the countries that have been analysed.

References

1. Hirsch, J.E. (2005) An index to quantify an individual's scientific research output. *Proceedings of the National Academy of Sciences of the United States of America* **102**, 16569–16572
2. ERA 2012 Journal List (2012) http://www.arc.gov.au/era/era_2012/era_journal_list.htm
3. Rowbotham, J. (2011) End of an ERA: journal rankings dropped. In *The Australian Higher Education*. 30 May 2011
4. Berlin principles on ranking of higher education institutions. http://www.che.de/downloads/Berlin_Principles_IREG_534.pdf
5. Gingras, Y. (2014) Criteria for evaluating indicators. In *Beyond Bibliometrics: Harnessing Multidimensional Indicators of Scholarly Impact* (Cronin, B. and Sugimoto, C.R., eds), pp. 109–125, MIT Press, Cambridge, MA
6. SCImago (2007) SJR: SCImago Journal and Country Rank. http://www.scimagojr.com (Retrieved 31 January 2011)

Research evaluation: improvisation or science?

Giovanni Abramo*[1] and Ciriaco Andrea D'Angelo[†2]

*Laboratory for Studies of Research and Technology Transfer, Institute for System Analysis and Computer Science (IASI-CNR), National Research Council of Italy, Italy

†Department of Engineering and Management, University of Rome 'Tor Vergata', Italy

Introduction

The proliferation of bibliometric indicators over recent years has generated a type of disorientation among decision-makers, who are no longer able to discriminate the pros and cons of the various indicators for planning an actual evaluation exercise. Performance-ranking lists at national and international levels are published with media fanfare, influencing opinion and practical choices. My impression is that these rankings of scientific performance, produced by 'non-bibliometricians' [1–3] and even by bibliometricians [4,5], are largely on the basis of what can easily be counted rather than 'what really counts'.

Performance, or the ability to perform, should be evaluated with respect to the specific goals and objectives to be achieved. The objectives must therefore be stated in measurable terms representing the desired outcome of production activity. The principal performance indicator of a production unit (whether this is an individual, research group, department, institution, field, discipline, region or country) is its productivity, or simply speaking the ratio of the value of the production output to the value of the inputs required to produce it. From this point of view, we will see that the renowned crown indicator and h-index (Hirsch-index), with its innumerable variants, and a wide variety of other publication-based and citation-based indicators, are inadequate to measure research productivity. As a consequence, all of the research evaluations based on these indicators and their relative rankings are at best of little or no value, and are otherwise actually dangerous due to the distortions embedded in the information provided to the decision-makers.

In the present chapter, we operationalize the economic concept of productivity for the specific context of research activity and propose a measurable form of productivity. From an economic perspective, we demonstrate the limits of the most commonly used performance indicators and present the indicator FSS (Fractional Scientific Strength), which better approximates the measure of research productivity. We present a methodology for measuring FSS at various levels of analysis. Finally, we will measure the performance of Italian universities by both FSS and the h-index, and will show the distortion inherent in the use of the h-index for assessing institutional productivity.

[1]Email: giovanni.abramo@uniroma2.it
[2]Email: dangelo@dii.uniroma2.it

Research productivity

Generally speaking, the objective of research activity is to produce new knowledge. Research activity is a production process in which the inputs consist of human, tangible (scientific instruments, materials, etc.) and intangible (accumulated knowledge, social networks, economic rents, etc.) resources, and where output, the new knowledge, has a complex character that is both tangible (publications, patents, conference presentations, databases, etc.) and intangible (tacit knowledge, consulting activity, etc.) in nature. The new-knowledge production function has therefore a multi-input and multi-output character. The principal efficiency indicator of any production is productivity, i.e. the ratio of the value of output produced in a given period to the value of production factors used to produce it. To calculate research productivity one needs to adopt a few simplifications and assumptions.

On the output side, a first approximation derives from the imposition of not being able to measure any new knowledge that is not codified. Secondly, where new knowledge is indeed codified, we are faced with the problem of identifying and measuring its various forms. It has been shown [6] that in the so-called hard sciences, the prevalent form of codification for research output is publication in scientific journals. Such databases as Scopus and WoS (Web of Science) have been extensively used and tested in bibliometric analyses, and are sufficiently transparent in terms of their content and coverage. As a proxy of total output in the hard sciences, we can thus simply consider publications indexed in either WoS or Scopus. With this proxy, those publications that are not censused will inevitably be ignored. This approximation is considered acceptable in the hard sciences, although not for the arts, humanities and a good part of the social science fields.

Research projects frequently involve a team of researchers, which shows in co-authorship of publications. Productivity measures then need to account for the fractional contributions of single units to outputs. The contributions of the individual co-authors to the achievement of the publication are not necessarily equal, and in some fields the authors signal the different contributions through their order in the byline. The conventions on the ordering of authors for scientific papers differ across fields [7,8], thus the fractional contribution of the individuals must be weighted accordingly. Following these lines of logic, all performance indicators based on full counting or 'straight' counting (where only the first author or the corresponding author receives full credit and all others receive none) are invalid measures of productivity. The same invalidity applies to all indicators based on equal fractional counting in fields where co-author order has recognized meaning.

Furthermore, because the intensity of publications varies across fields [9–11], in order to avoid distortions in productivity rankings [12], we must compare organizational units within the same field. A pre-requisite of any productivity assessment free of distortions is then a classification of each individual researcher in one and only one field. An immediate corollary is that the productivity of units that are heterogeneous regarding the fields of research of their staff cannot be directly measured at the aggregate level, and that there must be a two-step procedure: first, measuring the productivity of the individual researchers in their field, and then appropriately aggregating these data.

In bibliometrics, we have seen the evolution of language where the term 'productivity' measures refers to those based on publication counts, whereas 'impact' measures are those based on citation counts. In a microeconomic perspective, the first operational definition would actually make sense only if we then compare units that produce outputs of the same value. In reality, this does not occur because the publications embedding the new knowledge produced have different values. Their value is measured by their impact on scientific advancements. As a proxy of impact, bibliometricians adopt the number of citations for the units' publications, in spite of the limits of this indicator (negative citations, network citations, etc.) [13]. Citations do in fact demonstrate the dissemination of knowledge, creating conditions for knowledge spillover benefits. Citations thus represent a proxy measure of the value of output.

Comparing units' productivity by field is not enough to avoid distortions in rankings. In fact, citation behaviour too varies across fields, and it is not unlikely that researchers belonging to a particular scientific field may also publish outside of that field (a typical example is statisticians, who may apply statistics to medicine, physics, social sciences, etc.). For this reason, we need to standardize the citations of each publication with respect to a scaling factor stemming from the distribution of citations for all publications of the same year and the same subject category. Different scaling factors have been suggested and adopted to field-normalize citations (average, median, z-score of normalized distributions, etc.).

On the side of production factors, there are again difficulties in measuring that lead to inevitable approximations. The identification of production factors other than labour and the calculation of their value and share by fields is not always easy (consider quantifying the value of accumulated knowledge or scientific instruments shared among units). Furthermore, depending on the objectives of the assessment exercise, it could sometimes be useful to isolate and examine the contribution to output of factors that are independent of the capacities of the staff for the units under examination (for example, returns to scale, returns to scope, available capital, etc.).

The FSS indicator as a proxy of labour productivity

The productivity of the total production factors is therefore not easily measurable. There are two traditional approaches used by scholars to measure the total factor productivity: parametric and non-parametric techniques. Parametric methodologies are based on the *a priori* definition of the function that can most effectively represent the relationship between input and output of a particular production unit. The purpose of non-parametric methods, on the other hand, is to compare empirically measured performances of production units (commonly known as Decision Making Units or DMUs), in order to define an 'efficient' production frontier, comprising the most productive DMUs. The reconstruction of that frontier is useful to assess the inefficiency of the other DMUs, based on minimum distance from the frontier.

The measure of total factor productivity requires information on the different production factors by unit of analysis. Instead of total factor research productivity, most often research administrators are interested in measuring and comparing simply labour productivity, i.e. the value of output per unit value of labour, all other production factors being equal. In measuring labour productivity then, if there are differences of production factors other than labour available to each unit, one should normalize for these. Unfortunately, relevant data are not easily available, especially at the individual level. Thus an often-necessary assumption is that the resources available to units within the same field are the same. A further assumption, again unless specific data are available, is that the hours devoted to research are more or less the same for each individual. Finally, the cost of labour is likely to vary among research staff, both within and between units. In a study of Italian universities, Abramo et al. [14] demonstrated that the productivity of full, associate and assistant professors is different. Because academic rank determines differentiation in salaries, if information on individual salaries is unavailable then one can still reduce the distortion in productivity measures by differentiating performance rankings by academic rank.

Next, we propose our best proxy for the measurement of the average yearly labour productivity at various unit levels (individual, field, discipline, department, entire organization, region and country). The indicator is named FSS, and we have previously applied it to the Italian higher education context, where most of its embedded approximations and assumptions are legitimate.

As noted above, for any productivity ranking concerning units that are non-homogeneous for their research fields, it is necessary to start from the measure of productivity of the individual researchers. Without it, any measure at aggregate level presents strong distortions [12]. In their measures of these data, the authors gain advantage from a characteristic that seems unique to the Italian higher education system, in which each professor is classified as belonging to a single research field. These formally defined fields are called 'Scientific Disciplinary Sectors' (SDSs): there are 370 SDSs, grouped into 14 UDAs (University Disciplinary Areas). In the hard sciences, there are 205 such fields grouped into nine UDAs.

When measuring research productivity, the specifications for the exercise must also include the publication period and the 'citation window' to be observed. The choice of the publication period has to address often-contrasting needs: ensuring the reliability of the results issuing from the evaluation, but also permitting frequent assessments.

Labour productivity at the individual level

At the micro-unit level (the individual researcher level, R) we measure FSS_R, a proxy of the average yearly productivity over a period of time, accounting for the cost of labour. In equation 1 [1]:

$$FSS_R = \frac{1}{s} \cdot \frac{1}{t} \sum_{i=1}^{N} \frac{c_{ii}}{\bar{c}_i} f_i \tag{1}$$

where s is the average yearly salary of the researcher; t is the number of years of work of the researcher in the period of observation; N is the number of publications of the researcher in the period of observation; c_{ii} is the citations received by publication i; $\bar{c}_i$ is the average of the distribution of citations received for all cited publications of the same year and subject category of publication i; and f_i is the fractional contribution of the researcher to publication i.

We normalize by the average of the distribution of citations received for all cited publications because it proved to be the most reliable scaling factor [15]. Fractional contribution equals the inverse of the number of authors, in those fields where the practice is to place the authors in simple alphabetical order, but assumes different weights in other cases. For the life sciences, widespread practice in Italy and abroad is for the authors to indicate the various contributions to the published research by the order of the names in the byline. For these areas, we give different weights to each co-author according to their order in the byline and the character of the co-authorship (intra-mural or extra-mural). If first and last authors belong to the same university, 40% of citations are attributed to each of them; the remaining 20% are divided among all other authors. If the first two and last two authors belong to different universities, 30% of citations are attributed to first and last authors; 15% of citations are attributed to second and last author but one; the remaining 10% are divided among all others.

Calculating productivity accounting for the cost of labour requires knowledge of the cost of each researcher, information that is usually unavailable for reasons of privacy. In the Italian case we have resorted to a proxy. In the Italian university system, salaries are established at the national level and fixed by academic rank and seniority. Thus all professors of the same academic rank and seniority receive the same salary, regardless of the university that employs them. The information on individual salaries is unavailable, but the salary ranges for rank and seniority are published. Thus we have approximated the salary for each individual as the average of their academic rank. If information on salary is not available at all, one should at least compare research performance of individuals of the same academic rank.

The productivity of each scientist is calculated in each SDS and expressed on a percentile scale of 0–100 (worst to best) for comparison with the performance of all Italian colleagues of the same SDS; or as the ratio to the average performance of all Italian colleagues of the same SDS with productivity above zero. In general, we can exclude, for the Italian case, that productivity ranking lists may be distorted by variable returns to scale, due to different sizes of universities [16] or by returns to scope of research fields [17].

Labour productivity at the organizational level

We have seen that the performance of the individual researchers in a unit can be expressed in percentile rank or standardized to the field average. Thus the productivity of multi-field units can be expressed by the simple average of the percentile ranks of the researchers. It should be noted that resorting to percentile rank for the performance measure in multi-field units or for simple comparison of performance for researchers in different fields is subject to obvious limitations, the first being compression of the performance differences between one position and the next. Thompson [18] warns that percentile ranks should not be added or averaged, because percentile is a numeral that does not represent equal-interval measurement. Furthermore, percentile rank is also sensitive to the size of the fields and to the performance distribution. For example, consider a unit composed of two researchers in two different SDSs (A and B, each with a national total of ten researchers), who both rank in third place, but both with productivity only slightly below that of the first-ranked researchers in their respective SDSs: the average rank percentile for the unit will be 70. Then, consider another unit with two researchers belonging to another two SDSs (C and D, each with 100 researchers), where both of the individuals place third, but now with a greater gap to the top scientists of their SDSs (potentially much greater): their percentile rank will be 97. In this particular example, a comparison of the two units using percentile rank would certainly penalize the former unit.

However, the second approach, involving standardization of productivity by field average, takes account of the extent of difference between productivities of the individuals. In equation 2, the productivity over a certain period for department D, composed of researchers that belong to different SDSs [3]:

$$\text{FSS}_D = \frac{1}{RS} \sum_{i=1}^{RS} \frac{\text{FSS}_{R_i}}{\overline{\text{FSS}_{R_i}}} \qquad (2)$$

where RS is research staff of the department, in the observed period; FSS_{R_i} is the productivity of researcher i in the department; and $\overline{\text{FSS}_{R_i}}$ is the average productivity of all productive researchers in the same SDS of researcher i.

Distortion inherent in the use of the h-index for assessing institutional productivity

In a recent study, Abramo et al. [19] examined the accuracy of the popular h- and g (Egghe)-indexes for measuring university research productivity by comparing the ranking lists derived from their application to the ranking list from FSS. In the present chapter, we report an extract of that study. For every SDS, we identify the Italian universities included in the first quartile of the ranking by FSS, then check

Table I
Top universities by FSS that are not included in the same subset when performance is measured by h- and g-indexes

UDA	Percentage of top 25% universities by FSS not included in the same set by:	
	h-index	g-index
Mathematics and computer science	45	47
Physics	48	51
Chemistry	49	46
Earth sciences	42	35
Biology	42	36
Medicine	40	35
Agricultural and veterinary science	41	33
Civil engineering	28	26
Industrial and information engineering	40	35
Average	42	38

which of these would not be included in the same quartile under the rankings constructed with h and g values.

Table 1 presents the data aggregated by UDA. On average, the percentage of top 25% universities by FSS that are not included in the same set by h-index is 42%. Among the individual UDAs, the figures for these data vary between a minimum of 28% for the universities in civil engineering and a maximum of 49% for chemistry.

Concluding remarks

Until now, bibliometrics has proposed indicators and methods for measuring research performance that are largely inappropriate from a microeconomics perspective. The h-index and most of its variants, for example, inevitably ignore the impact of works with a number of citations below the h value and all citations above the h value of the h-core works. The h-index fails to field-normalize citations and to account for the number of co-authors and their order in the byline. Last but not least, owing to the different intensity of publications across fields, productivity rankings need to be carried out by field [20], when in reality there is a human tendency to compare h-indexes for researchers across different fields. Each one of the proposed h-variant indicators tackles one of the many drawbacks of the h-index while leaving the others unsolved, so none can be considered completely satisfactory.

The new crown indicator [MNCS (mean normalized citation score)], on the other hand, measures the average standardized citations of a set of publications. It is calculated as follows: one first calculates for each publication the ratio of its actual number of citations and the average number of citations of all publications of the same document type (i.e. article, letter or review) published in the same field and in the same year. One then takes the average of the ratios that one has obtained. The MNCS then cannot provide any indication of unit productivity. In fact, a unit with double the MNCS value of another unit could actually have half the productivity, if the second unit produced four times as many publications. Whatever the CWTS (Centre for Science and Technology Studies) research group [21] might claim for them, the annual world university rankings by MNCS are not 'performance' rankings, unless someone abnormally views performance as average impact of product, rather than impact per unit of cost. Applying the CWTS method, a unit that produces only one article with ten citations has better performance than a unit producing 100, where each but one of these gets ten citations and the last one gets nine citations. Furthermore, the methodology reported for producing the ranking lists does not describe any weighting for co-authorship on the basis of byline order. Similar drawbacks are embedded in the SCImago Institutions Ranking by their main indicator, the Normalized Impact (also known as Normalized Index), measuring the ratio between the average scientific impact of an institution and the world average impact of publications of the same time frame, document type and subject area. We do not consider further any of the many annual world institutional rankings that are severely size-dependent: the SJTU (Shanghai Jiao Tong University), *THES* (*Times Higher*

Education Supplement) and QS (Quacquarelli Symonds) rankings, among others. These seem to represent skilled communications and marketing operations, with the actual rankings resulting more from improvisation than scientifically reasoned indicators and methods.

The great majority of the bibliometric indicators and the rankings based on their use present two fundamental limitations: lack of normalization of the output value to the input value, and absence of classification of scientists by field of research. Without normalization, there cannot be any measure of productivity, which is the quintessential indicator of performance in any production unit; without providing the field classification of scientists, the rankings of multi-field research units will inevitably be distorted, due to the different intensity of publication across fields. An immediate corollary is that it is impossible to correctly compare productivity at international levels. In fact, there is no international standard for classification of scientists, and we are further unaware of any nations that classify their scientists by field at domestic level, apart from Italy. This obstacle can in part be overcome by indirectly classifying researchers according to the classification of their scientific production into WoS or Scopus categories, and then identifying the predominant category. FSS is a proxy indicator of productivity permitting measurement at different organizational levels. Both the indicator and the related methods can certainly be improved, but they do make sense according to the economic theory of production. Other indicators and related rankings, such as the simple number (or fractional counting) of publications per research unit, or the average normalized impact, cannot alone provide evaluation of performance; however, they could assume meaning if associated with a true measure of productivity. In fact, if a research unit achieves average levels of productivity this could result from average production and average impact, but also from high production and low impact, or the inverse. In this case, knowing the performance in terms of number of publications and average normalized impact would provide useful information on which aspect (quantity or impact) of scientific production to strengthen for betterment of production efficiency.

Aside from having an indicator of research unit productivity, the decision-maker could also find others useful, such as those informing on unproductive researchers, on top researchers (10%, 5%, 1%, etc.), top publications, dispersion of performance within and between research units, etc.

On the basis of the analyses above, we issue an appeal and recommendation. Our appeal to scholars is to concentrate their efforts on the formulation of productivity indicators more or less resembling the one we propose, and on the relative methods of measurement, aiming at truly robust and meaningful international comparisons. Our recommendation is to avoid producing research performance rankings by invalid indicators and methods, which under the best of circumstances serve no effective purpose, and when used to inform policy and administrative decisions can actually be dangerous. Our undertaking, as soon as possible, should be to develop a roadmap of actions that will achieve international performance rankings that are meaningful and useful to the research administrator and policymaker.

References

1. QS-Quacquarelli Symonds (2013) World University Rankings. http://www.topuniversities. com/university-rankings/world-university-rankings (Retrieved 26 July 2013)
2. SJTU, Shanghai Jiao Tong University (2013) Academic Ranking of World Universities. http://www.shanghairanking.com/ARWU2011.html (Retrieved 16 July 2013)
3. THES, Times Higher Education Supplement (2013) World Academic Ranking 2011–2012. http://www.timeshighereducation.co.uk/world-university-rankings/2011-2012/top-400. html (Retrieved 26 July 2013)
4. CWTS Leiden Ranking (2013) http://www.leidenranking.com/ranking (Retrieved 26 July 2013)
5. SCImago Journal and Country Rank (2013) Country Rankings. http://www.scimagojr.com/ countryrank.php (Retrieved 26 July 2013)
6. Moed, H.F. (2005) *Citation Analysis in Research Evaluation.* Springer, Dordrecht
7. Pontille, D. (2004) *La Signature Scientifique: Une Sociologie Pragmatique de l'Attribution.* CNRS Éditions, Paris
8. RIN (Research Information Network) (2009) *Communicating Knowledge: How and Why Researchers Publish and Disseminate Their Findings.* http://www.rin.ac.uk/our-work/ communicating-and-disseminating-research/communicating-knowledge-how-and-why-researchers-pu (Retrieved 26 July 2013)
9. Garfield, E. (1979) Is citation analysis a legitimate evaluation tool? *Scientometrics* **1**, 359–375
10. Moed, H.F., Burger, W.J.M., Frankfort, J.G. and Van Raan, A.F.J. (1985) The application of bibliometric indicators: important field- and time-dependent factors to be considered. *Scientometrics* **8**, 177–203
11. Butler, L. (2007) Assessing university research: a plea for a balanced approach. *Science and Public Policy* **34**, 565–574
12. Abramo, G., D'Angelo, C.A. and Di Costa, F. (2008) Assessment of sectoral aggregation distortion in research productivity measurements. *Research Evaluation* **17**, 111–121
13. Glänzel, W. (2008) Seven myths in bibliometrics. About facts and fiction in quantitative science studies. Proceedings of WIS Fourth International Conference on Webometrics, Informetrics and Scientometrics & Ninth COLLNET Meeting (Kretschmer, H. and Havemann, F., eds), Humboldt-University Berlin, Germany, 29 July–1 August 2008
14. Abramo, G., D'Angelo, C.A. and Di Costa, F. (2011) Research productivity: are higher academic ranks more productive than lower ones? *Scientometrics* **88**, 915–928
15. Abramo, G., Cicero, T. and D'Angelo, C.A. (2012) Revisiting the scaling of citations for research assessment. *Journal of Informetrics* **6**, 470–479
16. Abramo, G., Cicero, T. and D'Angelo, C.A. (2012) Revisiting size effects in higher education research productivity. *Higher Education* **63**, 701–717
17. Abramo, G., D'Angelo, C.A. and Di Costa, F. (2013) Investigating returns to scope of research fields in universities. *Higher Education* doi:10.1007/s10734-013-9685-x
18. Thompson, B. (1993) GRE percentile ranks cannot be added or averaged: a position paper exploring the scaling characteristics of percentile ranks, and the ethical and legal culpabilities created by adding percentile ranks in making "high-stakes" admission decisions. Annual Meeting of the Mid-South Educational Research Association, New Orleans, U.S.A., 12 November 1993
19. Abramo, G., D'Angelo, C.A. and Viel, F. (2013) The suitability of h and g indexes for measuring the productivity of research institutions. *Scientometrics* doi: 10.1007/s11192-013-1026-4
20. Abramo, G. and D'Angelo, C.A. (2007) Measuring science: irresistible temptations, easy shortcuts and dangerous consequences. *Current Science* **93**, 762–766
21. Waltman, L., Calero-Medina, C., Kosten, J. et al. (2012) The Leiden ranking 2011/2012: data collection, indicators, and interpretation. *Journal of the American Society for Information Science and Technology* **63**, 2419–2443

7

How global comparisons matter: the 'truths' of international rankings

Linda Wedlin[1]

Department of Business Studies, Uppsala University, Sweden

Introduction

International ranking lists of universities and higher education organizations are proliferating. This development consists of three main elements: (i) the number of rankings has multiplied; (ii) the scope of the rankings has increased to cover a larger number of universities in different parts of the world; and (iii) the rankings are attracting increasing global attention inside, as well as outside, the higher education field. There is widespread understanding that these rankings are influential, affecting everything from local university strategy-making, identity formation and reputation management, to national and even transnational policy-making on higher education and research matters. This has made rankings an important element in the development of a global governing field of universities. But what is it that makes rankings influential in this field?

The present chapter will elaborate on the role and impact of international rankings in the global higher education field. The aim is to increase our understanding of how rankings gain attention and legitimacy, and to analyse the implications of this development for the field of universities. To do this, I will attempt to shift focus in the ranking debate: from mainly centring on what the rankings measure, and how, and the methodological, and other, shortcomings of ranking systems, towards an emphasis on understanding the role and meanings attached to rankings as well as the dynamics of their development [1].

A ranking paradox

There is no lack of research on the development and implications of ranking systems, quite the contrary. A great number of studies have shown how rankings to an increasing extent are being used for governance purposes internally in universities: to promote and propel change and reform, as well as to show accountability and transparency towards different stakeholders [2]. Hazelkorn [3] has shown how nearly 60% of university managers claim that rankings have positively influenced the development of their institutions, and equally, many admit that

---

[1]Email: linda.wedlin@fek.uu.se

their universities have developed systems and procedures to analyse and make use of the ranking information. Similarly, Locke et al. [4] have shown through case studies of six British universities how rankings influence strategic decisions and governance procedures internally: by influencing the formulation of 'key performance indicators', shaping practices and procedures to collect, analyse and report data for the rankings, and, in some cases, by becoming strategic goals and targets in themselves.

Studies of rankings systems of business schools and law schools, two fields where rankings systems have been used for a long time and have been particularly influential, point to further influences of rankings on relations between organizations, and the development of entire fields. Studies have, for instance, pointed to the role of rankings in shaping organizational identities and identification processes among schools [5], where rankings form the basis for comparisons and positioning with others [6], and their role in creating and maintaining reputation and status within an international higher education market [7,8]. As a fundamental element, rankings constitute a commensuration process [9], whereby qualities of different entities become translated into quantitative common measures. This way, information is reduced and simplified, making complex relationships, conditions and qualities easy to present and compare. This shapes perceptions of quality, performance and worth, as well as beliefs about positions, value and relative standing among organizations [10].

However, a major part of the literature analysing academic rankings has focused on the rankings as measurement practices and has been "orientated towards correcting the flaws identified in rankings systems" [1]. The basis for much of this literature has been an assumed connection between rankings and quality: that rankings are created to measure, assess and compare quality of higher education institutions and offerings. Following this assumption, a wide range of criticisms of the rankings has been formed. Among these criticisms are the problem of quantifying inherently qualitative judgments; difficulties in measuring process and results in education; and the lack of contextual factors and account of cultural aspects of education. Researchers have also criticized the use of reputation as a proxy for quality in rankings, showing, for instance, the 'anchoring effects' of reputation, meaning that the rankings themselves guide subsequent assessments of reputation [11]. Significant critique has also been directed towards the validity of rankings: the choice and use of indicators and criteria and the weightings assigned to them [12,13]. Taken together, these studies, and a host of other writings on rankings, have provided a significant and robust critique of claims of measurement and quality inherent in global university ranking systems.

There is an apparent paradox in the development described above. This is owing to the fact that despite widespread discontentment and significant knowledge about the shortcomings of rankings, they are proliferating and becoming widely used by universities as well as by other actors in the higher education landscape. Universities and others shape actions and strategies deriving from them. Thus, as noted by Martins [14], the rankings are proliferating and being used regardless of their legitimacy. This paradox, I believe, requires an explanation and forms the baseline for my argument in what follows.

The 'truths' of rankings

The essence of my argument is that ranking systems build on and help to construct truths about reality. Such truths, however, need not be directly 'in accordance with fact or reality', meaning that the rankings produce one true and correct picture of the higher education field and its constitutive parts. Rather, we can consider truth to be 'a fact or belief that is accepted as true', thus following an alternative definition of 'truth' provided by the Oxford English Dictionary. With this concept of truth in mind, I consider the rankings as mechanisms that produce statements, opinions, images and beliefs that become accepted as true, concerning elements of the field such as the status of universities, their relative standing and their inherent qualities. Such truths, in turn, influence how we understand reality, regardless of whether these in fact correspond to any essential or 'real' quality or performance of higher education organizations or programmes. Both research and our experience tell us that any such relationship between ranking and quality and/ or performance is questionable [15,16].

The following sections will give three examples of the kinds of truths that the rankings produce. First, rankings build on and help to construct an understanding of the field of higher education as a global field. Secondly, rankings create a measurement for success, helping to shape and spread the idea of the 'excellent' university. Thirdly, the rankings help to construct measures and means of comparison, building the notion of competition among universities. In all of these cases, it should be noted that the rankings are neither the sole mechanism constructing and/or diffusing these images and truths, nor are they single-handedly responsible for the effects that these may have on the higher education field.

A global higher education field

One of the most marked features of the current ranking trend in higher education is its global character. Although ranking systems for higher education have been prominent in many countries and contexts for decades, for instance in the U.S.A. and the U.K., the past decade has witnessed a marked proliferation of international rankings and comparisons. The two best known of these are the ARWU (Academic Ranking of World Universities) produced by the Shanghai Ranking Consultancy in China and the World University Ranking produced by the British magazine *Times Higher Education*. These have been produced annually since 2003 and 2004 respectively. Since then, initiatives to rank and make competitive league tables and comparisons of universities worldwide have flourished.

Although not the first rankings of universities to appear, the ARWU and *Times Higher Education* rankings have had a significant impact on the field. The rankings have attracted increasing interest within and among universities around the world, and universities in varied contexts became interested in comparisons and assessments of themselves and others. At conferences, meetings and in networks, the issue of rankings is currently a prominent feature of university debates. Focused conferences on rankings have been organized yearly, for instance in Shanghai in

2007 and Leiden in 2009, and an IREG (International Ranking Expert Group) has been formed to lead the global discussion and development of rankings. The ranking debate has also spurred actors such as governments and international organizations to pay increasing attention to rankings [17]. A particular example is the European Union's effort to develop a new, comprehensive and multi-dimensional ranking of world universities (U-Multirank) [18].

These international rankings make a strong claim that higher education is global, and they carry the implicit assumption that universities (and in some cases other forms of higher education organizations) are comparable across countries, continents and institutional settings. The Shanghai rankings (ARWU) claim, for instance, to cover 500 universities from 43 countries in their ranking, and the ranking produced by QS (Quacquarelli Symonds) claims to cover 874 universities from 47 different countries. EduRoute makes an even more comprehensive claim in their 'G-factor' ranking, where 10000 universities in 172 countries are included. Although only the top 500 feature in the comparison on the web page, breakdowns into regional or country rankings can include larger sets of schools.

A slightly troubling aspect of this claim of globalism is that the 'global' character of this market is quite strongly skewed towards the North American, and to some extent the European, perspective on universities. In several of the leading international rankings, North American, mainly U.S., universities occupy the majority of the top 100 positions. In the ARWU 2013 ranking, 56 of the top 100 universities were North American, and only three non-U.S. schools managed to break into the top 20 (Cambridge, 5th; Oxford, 10th; and the Swiss Institute of Technology, 20th). In contrast, 33 European universities and 11 Asian/Australian ones occupy the remaining positions. A similar picture is given by the *Times Higher Education* World University Ranking, where 52 of the top 100 universities are North American, 32 are European and 16 are Asian/Australian.

With more than half of the top positions in these rankings being occupied by universities from only two countries (U.S.A. and Canada), they provide a very particular image of the global higher education field. To be fair, the rankings from QS and EduRoute have a slightly more diverse composition with only approximately one-third of the top universities originating in North America, adding nuance to the dominant image. But the overall impression, I believe, is unmistakeable: aggregating the scores from several of the leading international rankings, the North America dominance is apparent. No fewer than 91 of the top 300 universities worldwide (featuring in eight or more international rankings) are from the U.S.A. alone.

The image of a global higher education field has led universities and higher education organizations to pay increasing attention to aspects of interna-tionality, and they have come to see themselves as international players on a global university field. In my studies of international rankings in the field of business schools, I found how previously local or regional business schools began to claim that they were international, comparable with and in competition with leading American and other business schools across the world [6]. In particular, European business schools used the rankings as rhetorical devices to argue for their position and status in an international market for business education; using the rankings to argue for 'top' positions, 'world-leading' status, or, for lower-ranked schools, 'inclusion' in the global business school field [19]. In the business school rankings, as well as in several of the international university rankings (for instance *Times Higher Education* World University Rankings), various measures of internationality have become central aspects of what constitutes an international or global higher education organization.

Given the claims of global scope and reach of international rankings and the heightened awareness and orientation to an international market among higher education organizations, the image of a global market constructed by the rankings is both pervasive and powerful. The rankings build on as well as help to produce an image of a global field, in which universities and higher education organizations increasingly organize themselves to act as global players, despite the fact this this globalism appears to be rather limited in scope.

Measuring the excellent university

A dominant rhetoric in higher education is the notion of 'excellence'. To create excellence, and to aspire for excellence in research as well as in education and training, has been an explicit ambition both in policy and in practice for more than a decade [20]. Continuing to hold a prominent position in this debate, the notion of excellence was the key concept in a conference on higher education and research arranged during the Danish European Union presidency in the spring of 2012. The purpose of the conference was to discuss "how Europe can in the future finance and provide optimal conditions for excellent research", and to provide input to negotiations of the new framework programme for research, Horizon 2020 [21].

As one of the outcomes, the conference settled agreement on a set of guidelines for future policy work on higher education and research within the European Union and its members, collated in the 'Aarhus Declaration'. This declaration states that excellence in research "remains essential to *the future of Europe*", and "is the *essential foundation* that secures the development and availability of *human capital* to meet the needs of the future" [22]. Clearly a political target, ideas of excellence stretch well beyond the confines of the higher education field.

As a key organizational and political goal, the notion of excellence has served as a rationale for much reform in higher education and research systems across Europe, and perhaps the rest of the world, over the past decades. Among the clearest examples, we find Germany where the 'Excellence initiative', first carried out in 2006/2007, served to reform the university and higher education landscape. By injecting and distributing a significant amount of federal money to a few select institutions, a number of 'elite' universities were acknowledged and given resources to develop excellent research [23]. Continuing this path towards excellence, subsequent initiatives have identified and funded 'excellence clusters', giving significant resources to research units within these environments. Similar efforts to distinguish elite universities and promote excellence in research can be noted in several other European countries as well.

Table I
Comparison of toppers in four rankings [24–27]

Rank	Times Higher Education (2013)	ARWU (2013)	QS (2013)	EduRoute (2011)
1	California Institute of Technology	Harvard University	Massachusetts Institute of Technology	Massachusetts Institute of Technology
2	Harvard University	Stanford University	Harvard University	University of California, Berkeley
3	[=2] University of Oxford	University of California, Berkeley	University of Cambridge	Penn State University
4	Stanford University	Massachusetts Institute of Technology	University College London	University of Michigan
5	Massachusetts Institute of Technology	University of Cambridge	Imperial College London	Harvard University
6	Princeton University	California Institute of Technology	University of Oxford	National Autonomous University of Mexico
7	University of Cambridge	Princeton University	Stanford University	University of Wisconsin, Madison
8	University of California, Berkeley	Columbia University, NY	Yale University	Stanford University
9	University of Chicago	University of Chicago	University of Chicago	University of Pennsylvania
10	Imperial College London	University of Oxford	California Institute of Technology	University of Oxford
11	Yale University	Yale University	[=10] Princeton University	University of La Rioja
12	University of California, Los Angeles	University of California, Los Angeles	ETH Zürich/Swiss Federal Institute of Technology	Cornell University
13	Columbia University, NY	Cornell University	University of Pennsylvania	University of Washington
14	ETH Zürich/Swiss Federal Institute of Technology	University of California, San Diego	Columbia University, NY	University of Vienna
15	Johns Hopkins University	University of Pennsylvania	Cornell University	The University of Tokyo
16	University of Pennsylvania	University of Washington	Johns Hopkins University	Michigan State University
17	Duke University	The Johns Hopkins University	University of Edinburgh	Yale University
18	University of Michigan	University of California, San Francisco	[=17] University of Toronto	University of Santiago de Compostela
19	Cornell University	University of Wisconsin, Madison	Ecole Polytechnique Fédérale de Lausanne	Institute of Technology Bandung, Indonesia
20	University of Toronto	ETH Zürich/Swiss Federal Institute of Technology	[=19] King's College London	Columbia University, NY

As Readings [20] has noted, the term 'excellence' is an essentially empty concept, meaning it has no natural referent and no particular ideological content. The notion of excellence reaches beyond the related notion of quality, as it is inherently relational: everybody can have good quality, but only a few select ones can be excellent. On the other hand, the term excellence stops short of winning, since it is not exclusive and the terms of the rivalry are not necessarily clearly set.

This emptiness makes the concept of excellence useful as a political tool, but requires practices and procedures that can fill it with content. And efforts to do so are not lacking. The newly established ERC (European Research Council), for instance, has gone to great efforts to define the concept of 'scientific excellence', and establish criteria and evaluation practices to assess and determine research excellence in Europe, and to distribute funding accordingly. One of their aims is to "put excellence at the heart of European Research" [28], thus both promoting it as a political goal and defining the terms of its uses.

Serving a similar role, at least partly, the rankings have become one of the referents of excellence, both for universities and for policymakers. International rankings and their results are being used by university boards and managers in making strategic discussions and serve as input in formulating goals and defining key performance indicators, as noted above. Rankings and ranking results have also been used in national policy-making and priority-setting [29], as well as in debates within the European Union, in processes to defend, construct or revise a 'geo-political pecking order' of higher education systems around the world [30]. Table 1 compares the top 20 universities in four rankings [24–27].

As referents for excellence, rankings formulate and help to institutionalize measures for, and practices to assess, success. Even if there is great diversity across rankings as to what they measure and how, they propagate a somewhat coherent "global definition of academic quality" [31]. The core features of this definition include a focus on input measures, such as students, faculty and financial resources, and reputation as important criteria for success.

This has largely come to centre on measures of reputation as a proxy for quality, focusing on student surveys and judgments of quality, as well as on employer surveys and attempts to assess the 'employability' of graduates. In studies of the influence of rankings in management education, I and others have noted how this has resulted, among other things, in an increasing focus on marketing and PR, student services and career guidance in business schools across Europe [32]. Some rankings in this field explicitly aim to create measures to assess the financial value, also termed value-for-money, of academic education, leading to what could well be described as a shift from 'learning to earning' [33].

A particularly salient feature of this global definition of quality is also an emphasis on research and research production, particularly in the form of publications and citations. This trend is supported by the general proliferation of systems and practices for bibliometric analysis, which are spreading rapidly as quality measures in internal university evaluations, in national funding and quality-assurance systems, as well as in international rankings. These analyses build on and codify practices for evaluation and assessing research.

The widespread use of bibliometric analysis for public evaluations has led to the establishment and diffusion of simplified and often commercialized 'gold standards' for counting and valuing academic work. These include, for instance, 'A-journal' lists, 'FT-40 lists', 'journal impact factor' scores, and 'ISI Highly Cited' or 'Google scholar' counts. The FT-40 list, for instance, is the list of 40 journals that the *Financial Times* uses to measure research output in their annual MBA and business school rankings. This list is used in several European business schools as an explicit reference point for faculty publication assessment and strategies. Such simplified practices for bibliometric analysis have become a quick and relatively cheap way to create apparently 'objective' measures of academic success that may, in turn, influence publication strategies and research practices of individual as well as groups of researchers, including entire departments and universities.

Competition as the key to success

The field of higher education is undergoing a process of marketization whereby organizations increasingly adhere to and act on market logic and rhetoric [34]. In this field, the adherence to market ideals and principles is witnessed in the increasing production and use of quality measures and performance assessments, and a subsequent interest in measurements and assessments of value, particularly perhaps financial value, as noted above. This is further enhanced by the diffusion of a market and marketing rhetoric [35], an increasingly consumerist perspective on education [36], and a growing concern with producing relevant, useful and applicable knowledge to diverse audiences [37].

In this marketized higher education field, competition has become recognized as a key for success. Although managing competition, for students, faculty and resources, is a key strategic concern for university managers and leaders, creating competition and stimulating competition among universities, research groups and researchers are central activities for policymakers and regulatory agencies. As an example of the latter, the European research policy debate has been explicitly focused on the logic of the market and the ideas of competition. With the expressed aim to create Europe-wide competition among researchers and research groups and to promote 'excellence' in research, the launch of the ERC is a particularly clear example of this. In this sense, the notion of competition serves as a key to create both excellence and 'global success' in the market for higher education and research.

The logic of rankings follows this market ideology and rationale nicely, and clearly supports the idea of competition. A central argument in the promotion of rankings is the idea that there is a market out there to 'serve': a market where students are the customers and education is the product, and where other higher education providers are competitors. In this market, rankings serve as consumer-information tools, providing the market actors necessary information to make informed choices of where to study, where to invest resources, or where to go to work. And the notion of competition is, of course, central to any hierarchical ranking system: if one player moves up in a ranking list, another one must, by necessity, move down.

But rankings not only follow from ideas of the market. The development of international rankings has also helped to shape notions of competition, and created a basis for competition in the international field. How? First and foremost by creating comparability: the rankings have made it both possible and desirable to compare universities, programmes and courses across country and regional boundaries. By creating standardized measures of performance, applying them to a diverse set of universities and higher education organizations, and by reducing this information to a hierarchical ordering of universities, comparisons are both encouraged and facilitated. This has also led universities and, in my case, business schools, to form strategies and deploy resources to compete and to position themselves vis-à-vis other organizations. Much like what was noted above, this forms new comparisons globally, and thereby shapes organizational change and development.

The characteristics of the rankings, particularly their criteria for assessment, further suggest that the competition created and spurred by rankings is centred on issues of reputation. The hierarchical ordering of schools on the ranking list can be used to create, enhance or validate organizational reputation, and it shapes how external audiences value and assess the university and its offerings. Rankings also influence the positional status of universities, such that it becomes important to be equal to or better than those in your own perceived status group. Acting on these status and reputation cues provided by rankings, universities seem to become increasingly occupied with media, PR and marketing activities, as well as on issues of profiling and branding [38]. This may lead to what Gioia and Corley [39] describe as a "Circean transformation from substance to image".

Conclusion

Rankings have become associated with the powerful and pervasive images of a global and competitive higher education market. They gain influence in part because they help to explicate and codify dimensions of this market and the ensuing competition. But where, we may ask, will this ranking game take us, and is there an alternative?

The good news is that the image of the global field of higher education may be changing, albeit slowly. In the 10 years that international rankings have developed, the image of the field has become more diverse, in two respects. First, the number of universities featured in rankings has increased, and partic- ularly the number of universities from areas outside North America and Europe has increased. This is partly a result of an increasing number of rankings being produced and circulated, and that several rankings also have expanded in scope to include more schools into their ranking systems. However, the position of these universities also seems to be increasing slightly over time. Secondly, as a result of the increasing number of rankings systems in circulation, all with their respective criteria, methodology and measurement tactics, the criteria with which univer- sities are compared and assessed in public rankings is more diverse today than a decade ago. This allows, among other things, for selective attention to rankings and their assessments [40].

The bad news, on the other hand, is that change is both rather slow and rather limited in scope. It is still only changes in the margin in terms of altered positions, and there is still close to no inclusion of universities from, for instance, Africa or South America. There are also somewhat worrying standardizing tendencies in the rankings field, where efforts to set criteria and standards for ranking practices risk limiting the diversity of higher education evaluations through these systems. The recent effort of the IREG, for instance, represents an effort to set standards for ranking practices through an 'audit system' [41]. This seems not only to be a problematic endeavour, but also one that risks legitimizing existing ranking practices and limiting the scope for potential ranking alternatives.

Taken together, the proliferation and increasing influence of a 'rankings game' in global higher education is problematic on several accounts. Most significantly, they shape our own, as well as our audience's, expectations and assumptions about higher education and the universities. As a note of warning, we should be careful not to play along in this ranking game too far, or we may find ourselves in a situation where rankings alone define and determine our success. Instead, it is our responsibility to contemplate, construct and promote other, potentially more useful, models and methods to assess and evaluate quality, contribution and success in this field.

References

1. O'Connell, C. (2013) Research discourses surrounding global university rankings: exploring the relationships with policy and practice recommendations. *Higher Education* **65**, 709–723
2. Kehm, B. and Stensaker, B. (2009) *University Rankings, Diversity, and the New Landscape of Higher Education.* Sense Publishers, Rotterdam
3. Hazelkorn, E. (2007) The impact of league tables and ranking systems on higher education decision making. *Higher Education Management and Policy* **19**, 87–110
4. Locke, W., Verbik, L., Richardson, J. and King, R. (2008) *Counting What is Measured or Measuring What Counts? League Tables and Their Impact on Higher Education Institutions in England.* Higher Education Founding Council for England, Bristol
5. Elsbach, K. and Kramer, R.D. (1996) Members' responses to organizational identity threats: encountering and countering the business week rankings. *Administrative Science Quarterly* **41**, 442–476
6. Wedlin, L. (2007) The role of rankings in codifying a business school template: classifications, diffusion and mediated isomorphism in organizational fields. *European Management Review* **4**, 24–39
7. Sauder, M. (2006) Third parties and status position: how the characteristics of status systems matter. *Theory and Society* **35**, 299–321
8. Sauder, M. (2008) Interlopers and field change: the entry of the US News into the field of legal education. *Administrative Science Quarterly* **53**, 209–234
9. Espeland, W. and Stevens, M. (1998) Commensuration as a social process. *Annual Review of Sociology* **24**, 313–343
10. Wedlin, L. (2006) *Ranking Business Schools.* Edward Elgar, Cheltenham
11. Bowman, N. and Bastedo, M. (2011) Anchoring effects in world university rankings: exploring biases in reputation scores. *Higher Education* **61**, 431–444
12. Bowden, R. (2000) Fantasy higher education: university and college league tables. *Quality in Higher Education* **6**, 41–60
13. Usher, A. and Savino, M. (2007) A global survey of university league tables. *Higher Education in Europe* **32**, 5–15
14. Martins, L. (2005) A model of the effects of reputational rankings on organizational change. *Organization Science* **16**, 701–720
15. Devinney, T., Dowling, G.R. and Perm-Ajchariyawong, N. (2008) The *Financial Times* business school ranking: what quality is this signal of quality? *European Management Review* **5**, 195–208
16. Morgeson, F.P. and Nahrgang, J.D. (2008) Same as it ever was: recognizing stability in the Business Week rankings. *Academy of Management Learning and Education* **7**, 26–41
17. King, R. (2009) *Governing Universities Globally. Organisations, Regulation And Rankings.* Edward Elgar, Cheltenham

18. Van Vught, F. and Westerheijden, D. (2010) Multidimensional ranking: a new transparency tool for higher education and research. *Higher Education Management and Policy* **22**, 1–26

19. Wedlin, L. (2011) Going global: rankings as rhetorical devices to construct an international field of management education. *Management Learning* **42**, 199–218

20. Readings, B. (1996) *The University in Ruins.* Harvard University Press, Cambridge, MA

21. Horizon 2020. http://www.excellence2012.dk/horizon2020/ (Accessed 9 October 2013)

22. Aarhus declaration. http://www.excellence2012.dk/the-aarhus-declaration/ (Accessed 9 October 2013)

23. Weingart, P. and Maasen, S. (2007) Elite through rankings: the emergence of the enterprising university. In *The Changing Governance of the Sciences* (Whitley, R. and Gläser, J., eds), pp. 75–99, Springer, Dordrecht

24. The Times Higher Education World University Rankings 2013–2014. http://www.timeshigher education.co.uk/world-university-rankings/2013-14/world-ranking (Accessed 28 October 2013)

25. Academic Ranking of World Universities 2013. http://www.shanghairanking.com/ARWU2013.html

26. QS World University Rankings 2013. http://www.topuniversities.com/university-rankings/world-university-rankings/2013#sorting=rank+region=+country=+faculty=+stars=false+search=

27. EduRoute Top 500 universities in the world 2011. http://www.eduroute.info/Edu-world-university-rankings-top500.aspx

28. European Research Council. http://erc.europa.eu/mission (Accessed 28 October 2013)

29. Siganos, A. (2008) Rankings, governance, and attractiveness of higher education: the new French context. *Higher Education in Europe* **33**, 311–316

30. Kivinen, O. and Hedman, J. (2008) World-wide university rankings: a Scandinavian approach. *Scientometrics* **74**, 391–408

31. Dill, D. and Soo, M. (2005) Academic quality, league tables, and public policy: a cross-national analysis of university rankings. *Higher Education* **49**, 495–533

32. Wedlin, L. (2006) *Ranking Business Schools.* Edward Elgar, Cheltenham

33. Wedlin, L. (2004) Competing for employability. The media ranking of graduate business education. In *Learning to be Employable. New Agendas on Work, Responsibility and Learning in a Globalising World.* (Garsten, C. and Jacobsson, K., eds.), pp. 252–273, Palgrave, Basingstoke

34. Engwall, L. and Weaire, D. (2008) *The University in the Market.* Portland Press, London

35. Kirp, D. (2003) *Shakespeare, Einstein and the Bottom Line. The Marketing of Higher Education.* Harvard University Press, Cambridge, MA

36. Modell, S. (2005) Students as consumers? An institutional field-level analysis of the construction of performance measurement practices. *Accounting, Auditing and Accountability Journal* **18**, 537–563

37. Frank, D. and Meyer, J.W. (2007) University expansion and the knowledge society. *Theory and Society* **36**, 287–311

38. Drori, G.S., Delmestri, G. and Oberg, A. (2013) Branding the university: relational strategy of identity construction in a competitive field. In *Trust in Higher Education Institutions* (Engwall, L. and Scott, P., eds), pp. 134–147, Portland Press, London

39. Gioia, D. and Corley, K. (2002) Being good versus looking good: business school rankings and the Circean transformation of substance to image. *Academy of Management Learning and Education* **1**, 107–120

40. Sauder, M. and Espeland, W. (2006) Strength in numbers? A comparison of law and business school rankings. *Indiana Law Journal* **81**, 205–227

41. Hägg, I. and Wedlin, L. (2013) Standards for quality? A critical appraisal of the Berlin Principles for international rankings of universities. *Quality in Higher Education* **19**, 326–342

PART IV: JOURNALS, EDITORS AND PUBLISHERS

8

Metrics and evaluation in publishing

Nicola Gulley[1]
IOP Publishing, U.K.

Expansion and assessment

Publishing an article in a reputable journal has become intrinsically linked with research, both in terms of evaluation and communication. Indeed the core objectives remain the same today as they did in the very early days of publishing when Henry Oldenburg set up the very first journal in 1665; registration, dissemination, peer review and archival record [1]. Over the centuries, research expanded and the number of journals dramatically increased to meet this growing demand to publish. With this growth in journals, librarians and other decision makers required ways to evaluate and classify them, in terms of quality and perceived value to the community, to help prioritize between the journals. With the introduction of the Science Citation Index (SCI®), closely followed by the Journal Citation Reports (JCR®), a new way of indexing and measuring the impact of research was proposed. The development of SCI® and JCR® has been well documented in the literature (for an example see [2]).

To understand the scale in the growth, particularly from the late 1940s, we can look at the growth seen in the area of STM (science, technology and medicine) publishing. In a recent report by Ware and Mabe [3] on behalf of the STM, the International Association of Scientific, Technical and Medical Publishers, it was reported that there were approximately 28100 active scholarly peer-reviewed journals publishing around 1.8–1.9 million articles per year in 2011. They also reported that, on average, the number of articles published has grown, year on year, by approximately 3%; the number of journals by 3.5% and a corresponding growth in the number of researchers of 3%. In some research areas the growth has been much higher year on year. In physics and astronomy, for example, some years have seen growth rates as high as 13% compared with the previous year.

Journal metrics: part I

With so much choice, differentiating between journals is important for researchers in deciding where to publish, librarians when deciding which journals to buy and for publishers to benchmark their journals against the competition. Given that most researchers want to publish in a journal that not only reaches their key audience, giving them maximum visibility, but is also recognized as being prestigious by others both within and outside of their research field, a widely accepted metric

[1]Email: nicola.gulley@iop.org

can be attractive. The JIF (journal impact factor) is currently used as such a metric. It was introduced as part of the JCR® as one of the tools available for categorizing and evaluating journals and is effectively a measure of the number of citations of an average article published in the journal (a full definition is given at Thompson Reuters' Web of Knowledge [4]). Although it can be a useful metric, its meaning can vary from subject area to subject area, so it is important to understand what is being compared for any comparison to be meaningful. Research communities tend to have different citation habits, and from a publisher's, and authors', perspective this can cause problems when the JIF is used as a number in isolation without any reference to average JIF in a particular research field.

For example, the median JIF for a journal in mathematics is lower than that of a journal in the area of biology. As an example, one of the journals published by IOP Publishing, *Inverse Problems,* has a JIF of 1.866 in the 2012 JCR®. Over the years it has consistently been above the category median impact factor for the two categories in which it is indexed, 'Mathematics, applied' and 'Physics, mathematical' (2012 category median impact factors 0.742 and 1.138 respectively) and is highly regarded by the researchers who publish in the journal. Compare this with the median for the category biophysics at 2.605 and you can see that if *Inverse Problems* was compared with a journal below the median in biophysics without the context of where that value sat, it could be viewed in a more negative way than it deserves.

This is a very simplistic example, as the median JIF in a particular category will depend on many factors, but the point I am highlighting is that the JIF can tell you how many times on average an article in the journal will be cited, but in isolation it cannot tell you how that journal compares with others or how it is perceived by the research community. Therefore if a researcher is told that they should only publish in journals with a JIF above 2.0, it rules out very good journals in some fields, particularly where articles can accumulate as many citations outside of the JIF calculation window (2 years) as they do within it. However, the JIF continues to be used as a key metric of the success and quality of a journal. More recently, additional metrics such as the 5-year impact factor have been introduced to try and accommodate the areas that receive citations over a longer time period. Thompson Reuters have also run a number of presentations to explain how the JIF should be used ideally, and in the example referenced, they also outline a number of other metrics that can be used in conjunction with it [5]. There are also many other examples to be found in the literature and discussed elsewhere in this book.

More recently, with the move to electronic publishing in the mid-1990s, journals have also been evaluated on usage statistics such as the number of downloads (a download refers to a full-text article being downloaded by a reader). In the early days, the biggest challenge was how to benchmark these data to enable a meaningful comparison to be made between journals and publishers. In March 2002, an initiative called COUNTER (Counting Online Usage of Networked Electronic Resources) (http://www.projectcounter.org/index.html) was launched to set standards for recording and reporting usage statistics in a meaningful, and credible, way. COUNTER is a not-for-profit company and for a vendor to become COUNTER compliant there is a code of practice that should be followed [6]. However, there are no rules in COUNTER that govern article-level metrics, which is important in relation to new initiatives showing article-level downloads as a metric. The data can be compiled 'in the spirit' of COUNTER, but there are currently no set formats at this level, so it is difficult to compare article-level downloads across different platforms. However, there is a project that is underway (the Pirus project) to look at solutions to this.

Other factors that are taken into consideration when evaluating and comparing journals include the geographical and subject-area spread of the journal editorial board, as well as the specific subject scope of the journal. This varies from journal to journal and with the specific community they represent, but generally, an internationally respected journal will aim to have representation from all subject areas covered by the scope of the journal and a good balance of all the geographical areas where related research takes place. When evaluating a journal the geographical distribution of authors can also be a consideration.

Journal metrics: part 2

So far I have outlined what external metrics, both hard and soft, are used in assessing a journal, but there is another side to the story. With the significant growth of published articles, there have also been significant developments on the publishing side to monitor, manage and analyse the data that are accumulated as part of the infrastructure that supports publishing an article. At a publisher level, data on the geographical distribution of authors in journals are routinely collected as well as analyses of trends in journals. At IOP Publishing we run the peer review in-house for a number of journals with dedicated scientific editors. We maintain a database of a few hundred thousand referees for use across the journals using our systems. Internally, we can use these data to identify where we need more referees in particular countries or in particular subject areas. We collect data both at an article level and a journal level that is used to help develop the strategy for the journal. The editorial board members and editorial staff of the journals can review journal data including:

- The number of articles submitted to the journal over a time period
- The number of articles that do not make it through to publication
- Rejection/acceptance rates of the journal
- Processing times at different stages of the peer-review and publication process
- The number of downloads
- The number of citations
- The number of referee reports
- Geographical breakdown of authors/referees/readers
- The subject distribution

All of these data paint a detailed picture of a journal and supports the discussions around journal policies and development.

In addition to the specific development of journals, publishers can also provide some of these data at an institutional level that enables a librarian/ information scientists to build a better picture of the use of research published by their institute. There are different levels of information available. For example,

Elsevier has a service which integrates external information with the data it holds on its Scopus database, called SciVal, but many other publishers also offer bespoke reports based on the data they collect. It is an area that is developing as publishers, authors and research institutes review data available in addition to the traditional metrics that can help them develop a better idea of the impact of research and the success or failure of an investment. That investment can be anything from a technical development through to the output of a research grant; it comes back to the increasing pressure to find ways of reporting and evaluating on research investment in general.

There are also broader industry initiatives that provide additional data that help in this respect. One example is CrossRef (http://www.crossref.org/), which is an independent membership association founded and directed by publishers. CrossRef enables the linking of references in online documents that has greatly improved the navigation between published literature (predominantly peer-reviewed journal articles). It refers to itself as 'a sort of digital switchboard' which is an excellent description of how the links are managed as CrossRef does not hold full-text content, but facilitates the linking between different publishers. Since its foundation in 2000 it has also become the official DOI (digital object identifier) link registration agency for scholarly and professional publications. DOIs act as unique and persistent identifiers of digital content and can be used for objects other than journal articles, such as datasets. This is an interesting area that is developing in terms of wider linking outside of a standard journal article as the unit. For example services such as Figshare (http://figshare.com/faqs) are using DOIs to link and reference data, presentations, posters, etc.

From CrossRef, there are new publishing initiatives such as FundRef (http://www.crossref.org/fundref/) and ORCID (http:orcid.org/). FundRef is aiming to standardize the way that information on funding sources for research is captured and reported by developing a standard taxonomy for funders that can be captured as part of the publication process. This can then be deposited into a central database which can be made available for analysis. ORCID is aiming to develop a registry of unique research identifiers that researchers can use to link their research activities and output and will help to disambiguate work by researchers with the same or similar names.

Future metrics

Scientific publishing is currently undergoing one of the most radical changes in its history. I started the article by stating that the core objectives for journals have not changed in close to 350 years. Registration, dissemination, peer review and a reliable archival record are still fundamental to scientific publication, but the way this is achieved is changing. We are moving from analysing the performance of the journal as a unit to the article and, in some cases, to sections of the article. With the data accumulated and facilitated as part of the publishing infrastructure and the emergence of new ways of communicating in a digital environment, there is a need to find metrics that give a wider picture of the impact of a researcher's work. Blogs are becoming more important, and there are questions about how researchers managing vital databases get credit for the work they do when others use the data. Social media sites such as Twitter and Facebook are being used for discussions outside of the traditional channels and bookmark services such as Citeulike (http://www.citeulike.org) are used to index articles.

There have also been a number of new approaches to different aspects of scientific publishing. For example, *PLOS ONE* is a broad-subject journal that aims to assess whether articles submitted are technically sound before publication and facilitates comments post publication. *Atmospheric Chemistry and Physics* [7] uses a two-stage process of traditional peer review (reviewers specifically selected to review a paper) and comments collected online from an interactive public discussion. Other journals are experimenting with different formats such as video. *New Journal of Physics*, a journal published by IOP Publishing on behalf of the Institute of Physics and the Deutsche Physikalische Gesellschaft, introduced video abstracts following requests from authors for a more digital approach to explaining research in a broad-scope journal [8].

All of these different approaches require different ways of evaluation. How does a researcher get credit for a blog they write? How do you measure the impact of a video abstract? How can you measure the reach of article that has been forwarded on Twitter? Data on this are being captured, but not always presented publically. IOP Publishing, Springer, Nature Publishing Group and many other publishers are now presenting a range of data at an article level that covers citation counts, downloads, Twitter referrals, views, etc. Services such as Altmetric (http://www.altmetric.com) and Impactstory (http://www.impactstory.org/about) have been leading the way in looking at how to interpret these data. In a recent paper, Liu and Adie [9] describe how these alternative metrics can be used to complement the traditional citation analysis to build a more detailed picture of how research is used. Priem [10] goes further in his paper to discuss how this changing environment could affect scholarly publishing in the widest sense. He also addresses a number of concerns that have arisen in context of the alternative metrics being discussed, not least that they can be gamed. The metrics are also not easily benchmarked and there is currently little consistency across different websites.

A brave new world

Evaluation is useful for reviewing, measuring and improving the status quo. With more calls on resources available and limited financial constraints it becomes important to understand the outcomes of any investment. There have been a number of high-profile reviews of the processes supporting publication, from peer-review models through to wider access options such as open-access publication. Publishing and individual journals are also subject to ongoing evaluations as I have outlined above. However, there is also a need to ensure that the evaluation is clearly defined, and there are ongoing challenges with single metrics used out of context, a subject that is discussed in more detail in the bibliometrics literature than I have been able to cover in the present chapter.

Solutions have been found to new challenges as they arise, such as the COUNTER code of practice being introduced to give some standardization to the new metric of downloads, but there is more to be done in what is a very rapidly evolving environment, not only in defining agreed benchmarks, but also in making better use of the data already being accumulated that could be used as useful new metrics in conjunction with the more traditional ones.

For researchers there is the challenge of having reliable ways of reporting the impact of their research, however that is defined. The use of new ways of communicating research can be difficult to label within the confines of the traditional scholarly communication routes, but they are complementary and need to be recognized appropriately.

There are genuine concerns about the ease with which any one metric, such as downloads at an article level, can be manipulated or within the realm of social media where a 'like' or 'dislike' can be very subjective. And, of course, there are the ever-existing concerns that any metric can be taken out of context and misinterpreted. For example, if an article is picked up by a number of people and re-tweeted or has had an associated press release that increases the web traffic and download counts to that article, does it say anything more than that the article is popular at that particular time? Does it drive citations, indicate that the article is a high-quality article or that it is a popular article? All of the above? The usefulness of an article is decided over time by the relevant research community along with how well it is cited and used, but it does not mean that the additional information that can be provided at an article level is not useful when looked at in a broader sense. Citations, download counts, social media statistics, view of a video abstract, all of these metrics potentially tell a slightly different part of the overall story and could be used together to paint a fuller picture of the research.

Article-level metrics are still relatively new and evolving quickly, their long-term usefulness still hotly debated. Challenges with the existing traditional metrics have been well documented. Of course the answer is, as always, no single metric should be used in isolation, but in addition, there is another question to be answered about how useful some of the newer metrics will be in years to come. At the time of writing, *Nature* had just published a special issue on this topic [11] covering a number of related issues. *Scholarly Kitchen* had also covered this subject on a number of occasions, most recently in a blog post by Crotty [12]. So although there are still many questions about future metrics, what is certain is that this is set to be an interesting development that will evolve quickly and will continue to be debated for some time. With the continued focus on evaluation of research it will be important that these debates involve all of the different players. Journals are subject to evaluation, but publishers are also in a position to be supplying data and the infrastructure that could be useful in supporting a different approach to measuring a researcher's contributions in the future.

Acknowledgements

I am grateful for the support of IOP Publishing in writing this article, but any opinions expressed are mine and do not represent those of my employer or anyone else.

References

1. Mabe, M. (2006) (Electronic) journal publishing. The E-Resources Management Handbook UKSG. http://www.stm-assoc.org/2006_08_23_Electronic_Journal_Publishing.pdf (Accessed 20 October 2013)
2. Garfield, E. (2006) The history and meaning of the journal impact factor. *The Journal of the American Medical Association* **295**, 90–93
3. Ware, M. and Mabe, M. (2012) *The STM report: an overview of scientific and scholarly publishing.* http://www.stm-assoc.org/2012_12_11_STM_Report_2012.pdf (Accessed 23 October 2013)
4. Thompson Reuters, Web of Knowledge. http://wokinfo.com/essays/impact-factor/ (Accessed 21 October 2013)
5. Webster, B.M. (2009) About use and misuse of impact factor and other journal metrics. http://wokinfo.com/media/using-the-impact-factor.ppt (Accessed 21 October 2013)
6. COUNTER. http://www.projectcounter.org/ (Accessed 23 October 2013)
7. Atmospheric Chemistry and Physics: aims and scopes. http://atmospheric-chemistry-and-physics.net (Accessed 23 October 2013)
8. New Journal of Physics: video abstracts. http://www.njp.org/videoabstracts (Accessed 23 October 2013)
9. Liu, J. and Adie, E. (2013) New perspectives on article-level metrics: developing ways to assess research uptake and impact online. *Insights: the UKSG Journal* **26**, 153–158
10. Priem, J. (2013) Scholarship: beyond the paper. *Nature* **495**, 437–440
11. (2013) Research evaluation: impact. *Nature*, doi:10.1038/502287a. Also available at: http://www.nature.com/news/research-evaluation-impact-1.13949 (Accessed 23 October 2013)
12. Crotty, D. (2013) Driving altmetrics performance through marketing: a new differentiator for scholarly journals? The Scholarly Kitchen blog. http://scholarlykitchen.sspnet.org/2013/10/07/ (Accessed 23 October 2013)

9

The value and accuracy of key figures in scientific evaluations

Jan Reedijk[1]
Leiden Institute of Chemistry, Leiden University, The Netherlands

Introduction

The use of bibliometric analyses in the evaluation of research performances of scientists and groups of scientists has been common practice in many countries and for a number of decades already. Such analyses were initially performed by just counting the number of publications in refereed journals; during the 1970s, counting of citations became possible and fashionable, and even averaged numbers of citations per published paper started to be used by purchasing the services of certain specialized institutions.

With the now common and user-friendly availability of the WoS (Web of Science), searches, analyses and evaluations are possible and 'easily' being carried out by the non-expert. In fact, with competing sources for data mining and analysis (sometimes cheaper, but less complete, such as Elsevier's Scopus and Google Scholar) now, everybody with access to the Internet can do amateur evaluations of individual (and groups of) scientists. It is often not realized that the consequences for scientists (evaluation, salary, grants, etc.) can be quite dramatic, especially when such analyses are incomplete, or erroneous.

In many countries and universities, and even international organizations such as the European Union in the FP7 (Seventh Framework Programme), salaries and grants, or grant renewals, are quite directly determined by bibliometric figures. Irrespective of whether this development is desirable, the accuracy and value of such figures need to be unquestionable. However, it appears that increasingly the use of such evaluation appears to be more a matter of the 'values' of the numbers, and not anymore of real 'value'. It should also be realized that the more simplified and metric-driven the evaluation of scientific work becomes, the more susceptible science will be to fabrication, tricks and even fraud.

What types of values are relevant, and how prone they are for database errors, misuse and abuse will be discussed below. Some of these issues I have addressed in recent papers [1–3]; these and others are the subject of this account. A key issue of course should be that if bibliometric figures are used in evaluations, their meaning should be clear, their accuracy should be high, and they should allow a fair comparison between scientists who are working in the same field and that are of the same (scientific) age.

Accuracy is a very important issue of course. Given the fact that references are still largely imported manually in the WoS, where typos in names or initials

[1]Email: reedijk@chem.leidenuniv.nl

can easily miss papers by authors, the accuracy of papers and citations is far less then desired. In addition, it is a known fact that authors when citing papers make typos, and, even worse, may copy and paste poorly from other papers, thereby incorrectly citing references. Moreover, it is well known that Thomson Reuters may, or may not, change names of institutions, when authors have used uncommon or old names of their institutions. This may result also in missing citations.

Parameters used in evaluations of scientists: the impact factor of journals

It is generally agreed that scientists should publish, and the more papers a scientist has (co-)authored in highly ranked and highly respected scientific journals, the higher the appreciation for the scientist will be. Therefore I first need to discuss the value of the most commonly used impact factor, the 2-year impact factor published on the WoS by Thomson Reuters, nowadays also called TRIF (Thomson Reuters Impact Factor) [4].

In many evaluations, each paper of a certain author is given a multiplication factor, which could be just the most recent TRIF value, or an integer, arbitrarily determined. For instance, journals with a TRIF below 3.00 obtain a multiplication factor of 1, journals with a TRIF higher than 2.99 and lower than 6 obtain a multiplication factor of 3, and so on. As TRIF factors change by definition every year (see below), it is important that the correct values are used for past years (they cannot be found easily for more than 5 years back). Of course, the biggest uncertainty here is by far not the inaccuracy in the TRIF, but rather the fact that individual papers in a journal can have dramatic differences in citations. So when a paper is published in a journal with a TRIF value of 7 for that year, this does not imply that all papers in that journal in that year would have the same numbers of citations, namely 7!

Literature on definitions and use of impact factors are plentiful. The impact factors can cover 1, 2, 5 or more years, they can be generated from Thomson Reuters, from Google Scholar or from the Elsevier Scopus databases. I just give the common one from TRIF here, and I refer to others for details and critical discussion [4].

Say for the year 2012, TRIF = C/P, where C = *citations in 2012 to papers appeared in the journal during 2010 and 2011* and P = **citable** *publications in the journal during 2010 and 2011.*

To illustrate how risky the use of TRIF is when used for evaluations of a person, and also how meaningless TRIFs can be, I will discuss two recent examples of enormous jumps in TRIF lasting just 2 years (first up and, 2 years later, down again), each as the result of 'explosions' caused by a single article.

This jump happens when a super-hot (usually methodological or review) paper is cited extremely frequently. This high citation first may have an effect on the immediacy index, but subsequently, the TRIF jumps up and after that will go down again, just from the effect of that single paper. The two examples below from recent years clearly illustrate this effect; I already alluded briefly to one of these in 2012, even before the TRIFs for 2011 had been published [2]; TRIFs for 2012 appeared in June 2013 [5].

The first example deals with a methodological paper by Westrip [6], published in 2010 in the *Journal of Applied Crystallography*, a journal with some 200 papers per year. This single paper generated a huge number of citations already in 2010, but in particular in 2011, it received 712 citations, compared with 1086 citations made to all other 191 papers from 2010 in that journal. The consequence is a significant jump in TRIF, as seen in Figure 1.

An even more striking case is the paper by Sheldrick [7], a leading crystallographer. With his paper from 2008 in *Acta Crystallographica Section A*, a specialist journal, with approximately 50–70 papers each year, he generated a citation explosion bringing the TRIF in 2009 and 2010 up to 50 or higher, whereas before 2009 it was around 2, and, as was predicted beforehand, for the TRIF 2011 it returned to around 2 again (Figure 2). The paper was published in January 2008; the citations to it were: 3521 (in 2008), 4891 (in 2009), 6937 (in 2010), 8181 (in 2011) and 4816 (in 2012). It should be noted that the still high number of citations to this paper in 2012, by definition does not contribute to the TRIF 2011. From all the citations to this 2008 paper, only the citations obtained in 2009 and 2010 have an effect on the TRIF. That is, 11 828 citations to some 200 papers, and 95% of these are to this single paper!

It should be evident that the scores of these two single papers do not say anything at all about the quality (or citations) obtained by the other papers in that journal during these 2 years, although the jump in TRIF would suggest to many bureaucrats, administrators and even scientists that all papers in that journal were responsible for the increase in TRIF to 50! This misconception may also have a dramatic effect on the evaluation of scientists in the field, as I will show now.

A hypothetical, but not unrealistic example to illustrate financial consequences: assume two authors in the same field, A and B, being equal in age, experience and quality. They each publish two papers in the above-mentioned *Acta Crystallographica Section A* and these two papers appeared within 1 month for each author. Coincidentally, author A has published the first paper in December 2008 and the second paper in January 2011; author B has published the first paper in January 2009, and the second in December 2010. Irrespective of the fact that

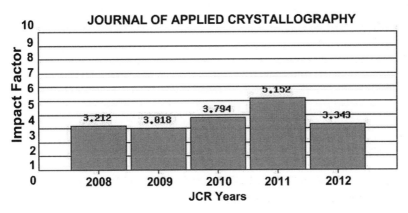

Figure 1

TRIFs for *Journal of Applied Crystallography* from 2008 to 2012
The temporary increase in 2011 is the result of the large number of citations to a single paper in 2010 [6].

Figure 2

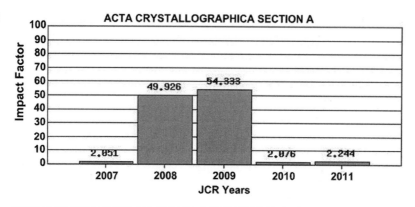

TRIFs for *Acta Crystallographica Section A* from 2007 to 2011 [7].

whether these four papers are cited a lot, or perhaps not at all, the papers of author B would have been 'multiplied' by a factor of 50 in value; if she/he lives in a country where the salaries and grants are related to papers and high TRIF values, then B would have earned a fortune, whereas A would not have received this bonus!

These are just a few cases to emphasize that the TRIF value for a journal in a certain year does *not* imply that all papers in that journal over that year have the same quality. The TRIF of a journal is just a surrogate measure of the quality of its papers. It only shows their **average** citations. As early as 2005, *Nature* [8] wrote in an editorial: "Research assessment rests too heavily on the inflated status of the impact factor." They calculated that just 25% of the published articles in the period at hand contributed to 89% of the journal's 2005 impact factor [8]. Nevertheless, the process still goes on! And when the process continues, editors will find clever, but not always seen as fair, ways to optimize the TRIF, as discussed elsewhere [2,3]. Of course, we should not discourage our scientists from publishing in high-impact journals. We only should realize that for individual papers, a high-impact paper is not equivalent to the TRIF value of the journal.

At this point, I also want to mention another journal comparison parameter, SNIP (source normalized impact per paper), introduced by Moed [9]. SNIP measures the contextual citation impact of a journal, taking into account characteristics of its properly defined subject field, especially the frequency with which authors cite other papers in their reference lists. It covers in particular the rapidity of the maturing of the citation impact. Readers interested in this rapidly evolving discussion are referred to the original paper of Moed [9] and to later papers citing this work. Also, publishers' websites, such as Elsevier with SciVerse and Scopus, deal with recent developments in other parameters.

Parameters used in evaluations of scientists: the h (Hirsch)-index for (groups of) persons

A very recently and successfully introduced parameter is the h-index (h). The definition of h is as follows [10]: "*The number of papers (h) by the scientist that have received at least h citations in a given period.*"

Although initially set up for a single scientist, and meant for a whole career [10], the h-index can also equally well be used for groups of scientists, for a certain period, and even for a journal. Later, several derivatives of the standard h-index were also proposed [11–14]; they are not discussed in the present chapter. For an alternative to h-index, see a new suggestion by Bornmann [15] proposing the indicator $P_{top10\%}$ as a better substitute for the h-index. $P_{top10\%}$ is the number of publications which belong to the top 10% of most frequently cited publications. So a publication belongs to the top 10% of the most frequently cited only if it is cited more frequently than 90% of publications published in the same subject area and in the same year. Just like the h-index, $P_{top10\%}$ provides information about productivity and citation impact in a single number. So it just gives the number of publications for an author that are of major significance [15]. Whether this will supersede the h-index remains to be seen of course.

The (meanwhile) standard h-index appears to be very simple to calculate, one would think, but often it is not! The value of h can be used by research councils, for instance to allow submission of certain grant applications only for scientists with an h-value above a certain threshold number. The major caveats here are numerous. Let me just mention the following ones:

1. The standard h-index is age dependent; it can only increase over time; so older scientists generally have higher h-indices than younger colleagues in the same field.
2. The h-index is strongly research-field dependent; in some fields the number of citations per paper on average is much lower (as in mathematics) than in other fields (such as clinical medicine).
3. Citations to papers are necessarily all positive or relevant.
4. Scientists with a common name and common initials can have colleagues with the same name and initials, so their citations and papers are added up or mixed up. Even Thomson Reuters does so! Just to illustrate, the top 12 most-cited chemists worldwide, according to WoS on 1 May 2013 are all 'persons' with the names: Wang (J, Y and L), Kim (J), Zhang (L, J and Y), Liu (Y), Li (Y and J) and Chen (Y), i.e. all typical 'multiple' persons. In the current top 20, in fact only three 'single scientists' are present.
5. The h-index does not take into account the number of authors on any paper.
6. The h-index also does not consider the real numbers of citations.
7. The h-index is biased towards researchers that are active in writing review articles.

The use of the h-index and its many derivatives [14] has been critically discussed many times, and this will not be repeated here. Interested readers are referred to comments of Waltman, Marx and others [11,12,16] and many references cited there. To illustrate the large number of discussions: as many as 923 journal articles in the WoS by 1 May 2013 have 'h-index' in the title. The original Hirsch paper [10] had been cited over 1200 times by 1 May 2013, i.e. much more than any of Hirsch's research papers since 1960.

In addition to h values generated from the WoS (Thomson Reuters), Elsevier Scopus and Google Scholar also now allow the generation or calculation of h values, either directly at their website (Scopus), or via third-party software [17], or using a personal profile (Google Scholar). It appears that the values generated from Scopus or Google Scholar can differ significantly from those of Thomson Reuters, especially for older scientists, as Thomson Reuters has the most complete database of older papers. More importantly, problems do occur with authors who have over 1000 documents (Google Scholar), or with authors having common names and initials (all databases) so that proper filtering is required. It should be noted that from the database of Google Scholar, the h value can only be calculated for yourself and after generating an author profile. The use of a software package from Harzing [17] allows a quick, albeit less accurate, method to find h values. Unfortunately, such a search appears to be full of errors (more documents, and thus more, incorrect, citations in many cases). Moreover, for searches for names such as 'John Smith' or 'Peter Williams', it is almost impossible to perform quick analyses of the h-index using this software package [17], despite the rapid improvements of this site.

As a test case, I have checked my own data for the three databases, as per 1 May 2013. By using WoS, I arrive at a value of **79**. Elsevier Scopus makes it only **66**, and using Google Scholar after having generated a personal profile and removed manually non-research papers and chapters not belonging to me, this public value reaches **74** for me.

I have also performed the same analyses for 8 chemists, all having unique names and initials and working in my own fields of interest, but presented anonymously here. The quite large and striking variations in outcome are detailed in Table 1 below.

In the case of Google Scholar, too many 'papers' are found, as they include book chapters and patents, but often also concern just internal papers or local ones, or the hits even include all chapters of an edited book. For a more detailed comparison between WoS and Google Scholar, I refer to the Publish or Perish website [17].

The main general conclusion from the data in Table 1 is that quite large variations in h values are found, depending on the database used, for the same

Table 1
Differences in the h-index, calculated from different sources, as per 1 May 2013

Database		WoS		Scopus		Google/Harzing	
Name	Sub-field	Papers (n)	h	Papers	H	Documents	h
Author 1	Materials	587	83	553	75	886	89
Author 2	Organic	409	74	343	65	760	83
Author 3	Catalysis	356	55	377	54	527	58
Author 4	Inorganic	259	48	231	41	314	47
Author 5	Inorganic	224	33	180	29	251	33
Author 6	Organic	291	39	295	41	352	41
Author 7	Organic	676	88	584	81	888	91
Author 8	Organomet	208	47	198	31	297	43

WoS and Scopus data were directly taken from their websites. Google Scholar data were taken via the Publish or Perish software from Harzing [17].

scientist. Therefore the use of h values should not be recommended for use in evaluations, certainly not when the data generation is performed by non-specialists, or when the source is not indicated, and certainly not when the scientists have not been allowed to check the data before use.

Misuse and abuse

It is now increasingly common that metrics are used in evaluations of scientists, and that often only simple parameters are used. Therefore the temptations to try to influence these parameters will increase, and fabrication or engineering of data may be the result. So it can be predicted that the more simplified and metric-driven the evaluation of scientific work becomes, the more susceptible science will be to fabrication of data, tricks and even fraud.

To generate increases in the TRIF of their journal, editors can use methods where citations to the previous 2 years (i.e. those contributing to TRIF) are added in editorials, or they simply invite more reviews, which are known to be cited more in the first few years. Or they can encourage authors to 'not forget to cite this journal'. In case editors behave unethically in this respect, Thomson Reuters may temporarily remove (de-list or suppress) the journal from their annual listing in JCR (Journal Citation Reports); in fact, they have done so already in a quite few cases during the last decade [18]. A striking case is the *Journal of Gerontology*, where the departing editor in an editorial cites many papers from the previous 2 years [19]. According to the JCR website [20], the 2013 title-suppression list contained about 50 journals. Some journals, however, seem to challenge this behaviour of Thomson Reuters [21], as is also discussed in detail at The Scholarly Kitchen website [22].

Not really misuse or abuse, but certainly not correct is the following case. In the European Union FP7, the bureaucrats ask, or encourage, that applicants mention in their application, as part of their CV, the TRIF (of the journal for each of their papers). This should of course be the TRIF of the year when the paper was published. However, FP7 does not require such details, and as a result, applicants will most likely mention the most recent TRIF, even for papers that appeared a decade ago. Most journals have shown increasing TRIF values over the years, simply because the general trend in all fields is that the number of references per paper is increasing each year.

To increase the personal h value, certainly when the number is still low, say below 15 or 20, one could ask friends and colleagues to preferentially cite one's papers, or also increase self-citations. This is indeed also to be seen as unethical behaviour, but I am fairly sure it has been done and will still be done.

Concluding remarks

As shown above, scientific evaluations of scientists, groups of scientists, institutions and also journals are increasingly performed with the use of a single parameter, be it a so-called h-index for (groups of) scientists, or the TRIFs of the journals that the scientist(s) at hand used to publish their research results.

It was shown that the use of such parameters is full of risks, not only owing to often-significant inaccuracies and errors, but nowadays increasingly also because such parameters are subject to manipulation/fabrication. In fact, nowadays many organizations try to develop and use indices by counting things that can be counted, rather than considering factors that cannot be counted, but that are much more important. So it is to be expected that evaluations will probably become more and more a matter of values (numbers), and less so of value. For the time being, it is very important to be aware of these uses and consequences. For authors, I would therefore make the following recommendations.

1. If authors select a journal to submit a paper, they should not pay much attention to the (most recent) TRIF of the journal.
2. Authors should never change (the spelling of) their name (females) or initials or hyphenation (Hispanics) after a first publication has appeared; it may cost citations. Also authors should carefully check the spelling of their name in papers where they are a non-submitting co-author.
3. If scientists have to provide an h-index for their work at a certain date, they should always mention the measuring date and the database from which this value of h was generated.

Finally, I would also provide a few recommendations for science evaluators, selection committees, research councils and university boards.

1. Never use single parameters to evaluate scientists and applicants for jobs or grants. Realize that the data behind the derived parameters can be incorrect. I warned about this many years ago, as far back as 1998 [23], and my warnings were followed by those of many others [4,11,16,24–27] and I am far from being complete here. At this point, I should particularly mention also a recent initiative, received after writing the present chapter, coined the 'San Francisco Declaration on Research Assessment' (or DORA) from May 2013, signed by a large number of editors in the field of cell biology and with a petition to Thomson Reuters to change the journal impact factor significantly. For details and links, see their website regarding JCR numbers [28].
2. In case numerical data are desired to assist your scientific assessments, make sure you have professional assistance, and most importantly have the involved scientists themselves check such data, before they are used in evaluations. If one requires applicants to provide an h value, have the method of calculation (WoS, Scopus or Google Scholar) and the measuring date be explicitly mentioned.
3. Given the fact that citation data and parameters derived from such data can be manipulated and engineered, and that there are no reasons to assume that such engineering can be stopped, great care should be taken, also by the experts, in using numerical data for evaluations of individual scientists, departments and universities.

References

1. Reedijk, J. (2012) Citations and ethics. *Angewandte Chemie International Edition* **51**, 828–830
2. Moed, H.F., Colledge, L., Reedijk, J., Moya-Anagon, F., Guerrero-Bote, V., Plume, A. and Amin, M. (2012) Citation-based metrics are appropriate tools in journal assessment provided that they are accurate and used in an informed way. *Scientometrics* **92**, 367–376
3. Reedijk, J. and Moed, H.F. (2008) Is the impact of journal impact factors decreasing? *Journal of Documentation* **64**, 183–192
4. VanClay, J. (2012) Impact factor: outdated artefact or stepping stone to journal certification. *Scientometrics* **92**, 211–238
5. Thomson Reuters (2013) Release of Journal Citation Reports, 2012 Citation Data In Journal Citation Reports®. http://admin-apps.webofknowledge.com/JCR/static_html/notices/notices.htm
6. Westrip, S.P. (2010) publCIF: software for editing, validating and formatting crystallographic information files. *Journal of Applied Crystallography* **43**, 920–925
7. Sheldrick, G.M. (2008) A short history of SHELX. *Acta Crystallographica Section A* **64**, 112–122
8. Editorial (2005) Not-so-deep impact. *Nature* **435**, 1003–1004
9. Moed, H.F. (2010) Measuring contextual citation impact of scientific journals (SNIP). *Journal of Informetrics* **4**, 265–277
10. Hirsch, J.E. (2005) An index to quantify an individual's scientific research output. *Proceedings of the National Academy of Sciences of the United States of America* **102**, 16569–16572
11. Abramo, G., D'Angelo, C.A. and Viel, F. (2010) A robust benchmark for the h and g indices. *Journal of the Association for Information Science and Technology* **61**, 1275–1280
12. Bornmann, L. and Marx, W. (2013) How good is research really. *EMBO Report* **14**, 226–230
13. Molinie, A. and Bodenhausen, G. (2010) Bibliometrics as weapons of mass citation. *Chimia* **64**, 78–89
14. Bornmann, L., Mutz, R., Hug, S.E. and Daniel, H.D. (2011) A multilevel meta-analysis of studies reporting correlations between the h index and 37 different h index variants. *Journal of Informetrics* **5**, 346–359
15. Bornmann, L. (2013) A better alternative to the H index. *Journal of Informetrics* **7**, 100
16. Waltman, L. and van Eck, N.J. (2012) The inconsistency of the h index. *Journal of the Association for Information Science and Technology* **63**, 406–415
17. Harzing, A.W. (2007) Publish or Perish. http://www.harzing.com/pop.htm
18. Agrawal, A.A. (2005) Corruption of journal impact factors. *Trends in Ecology & Evolution* **20**, 157
19. Morley, J.E. (2004) Flying through 5 years. *Journals of Gerontology. Series A, Biological Sciences and Medical Sciences* **59**, 1270–1276
20. JCR (2013) Suppression list Journals. *Journal Citation Reports®.* http://thomsonreuters.com/press-releases/062013/2013-journal-citation-reports
21. van der Wall, E.E. (2012) The NHJ 2012 in retrospect: which articles are cited most. *Netherlands Heart Journal* **20**, 481–482
22. Davies, P. (2013) *Netherlands Heart Journal* editor delivers Dutch citation treat. http://scholarlykitchen.sspnet.org/2013/01/30/netherlands-heart-journal-editor-delivers-dutch-citation-treat/
23. Reedijk, J. (1998) Sense and nonsense of science cititation analyses: comments on the monopoly position of ISI and citation inaccuracies. Risks of possible misuse and biased citation and impact data. *New Journal of Chemistry* **22**, 767–770
24. Bornmann, L., Mutz, R. and Daniel, H.D. (2008) Are there better indices for evaluation purposes than the h index? A comparison of nine different variants of the h index using data from biomedicine. *Journal of the Association for Information Science and Technology* **59**, 830–837
25. Bornmann, L., Mutz, R. and Daniel, H.D. (2009) Do we need the h index and its variants in addition to standard bibliometric measures? *Journal of the Association for Information Science and Technology* **60**, 1286–1289
26. Ernst, R.R. (2010) The follies of citation indices and academic ranking lists. A brief commentary to 'Bibliometrics as Weapons of Mass Citation'. *Chimia (Aarau)* **64**, 90
27. Kotov, N.A. (2010) Fraud, the h-index, and Pasternak. *ACS Nano* **4**, 585–586
28. San Francisco Declaration on Research Assessment (draft). http://tagteam.harvard.edu/hub_feeds/119/feed_items/165388

10

On the quality of quality assessments

Lars Engwall[1]

Department of Business Studies, Uppsala University, Sweden

Introduction

A main thread throughout the present volume is the tendency in the scientific world to increasingly rely on bibliometrics in the evaluation of academic institutions as well as individual scholars. Impact factors, based on the citations of articles in specific journals during a 2-year period, have become important for publishers for the prestige of their journals and at the end of the day for subscription figures and subscription rates. These impact factors in turn have strong effects on the publishing behaviour of researchers, who for natural reasons, try to be published in journals with as high impact factors as possible. As a result, in many scientific fields today, academic institutions have outsourced the task of making the quality assessments to journal editors and their reviewers. Although earlier evaluations of candidates on the academic job market in many instances were based on the reading of their publications, current evaluations are increasingly based on the impact factors of the journals where the research has been published. Such an approach has the advantage of efficiency of course: comparing numbers of publications weighted by their impact factors is clearly much less time-consuming than providing a personal opinion after careful reading. However, the use of bibliometrics for evaluations rests on one very vital assumption, i.e. that the quality assessments made by journal editors and their reviewers can be trusted. The present chapter will point to the fact that this is not always true and will provide an analysis of the quality of the quality assessments provided by journal editors and their reviewers. In so doing, it will point to two types of errors: first, the reject error, i.e. the rejection of papers that eventually appear to be very important, and secondly, the accept error, i.e. the acceptance of papers that eventually turn out to be fraudulent. For both types of errors, examples will be presented. In addition, the present chapter will point to the risk that these errors may increase in number with the passage of time. It is argued that the peer-review system is gradually deteriorating for two reasons: first, the radically increasing flow of manuscripts, and secondly, the intensified pressure on individuals to publish. The former circumstance will imply that the demand for reviewers is increasing, whereas the latter has the consequence that the supply of reviewers is decreasing. Also, in this case, empirical evidence will be provided. The final section discusses the conclusions.

[1]Email: lars.engwall@fek.uu.se

Errors in the review system

In analysing the review system, it is appropriate to recall the risks involved in statistical testing (Figure 1, left-hand panel) [1]. It refers to two types of errors: type I error, implying that a correct hypothesis is rejected, and type II error implying that a false hypothesis is not rejected. As shown in the right-hand panel of Figure 1, the same type of problems appears in the review system. The type I error implies that an important significant contribution is rejected (reject error), whereas the type II error means that bad papers are accepted (accept error). In the following two subsections, I will discuss these two errors, respectively.

The reject error

Since reviewers are likely to be conservative in their quality assessments, reject errors can be expected to occur widely, although they are more difficult to identify than accept errors. However, an illustration of the occurrence of reject errors is the experiment performed by the two psychologists Douglas P. Peters and Stephen J. Ceci some 30 years ago [2]. They selected 12 articles, which had already been published in 12 highly regarded psychology journals, and sent them back for review 18–32 months after their publication. They then found that out of 38 editors and reviewers, only three detected the resubmissions. Only one of the nine remaining articles was accepted. Of the 18 referees, 16 recommended reject, in many cases referring to "serious methodological flaws".

There are also a number of rather spectacular non-experimental examples of reject errors. The 1977 Nobel Laureate for Physiology or Medicine, Rosalyn S. Yalow, pointed out in her Nobel Lecture that she, and her long-time collaborator, Solomon Berson (who could not share the prize since he died in 1972), had difficulty in publishing their results [3]:

> "*we were able to demonstrate the ubiquitous presence of insulin-binding antibodies in insulin-treated subjects* [...] *This concept was not acceptable to the immunologists of the mid-1950s. The original paper describing these findings was rejected by* Science *and initially rejected by the* Journal of Clinical Investigation [...] *A compromise with the editors eventually resulted in acceptance of the paper.*"

Figure 1

Statistical Testing			Reviewing		
Action	H_0 is True	H_0 is False	Action	Good Paper	Bad Paper
Reject	Type I Error	Correct	Reject	Reject Error	Correct
Accept	Correct	Type II Error	Accept	Correct	Accept Error

Errors in statistical testing and in review systems

Berson and Yalow shared early rejections with another Nobel Laureate for Physiology or Medicine, Hans Krebs, who received the prize in 1953. His paper on his path-breaking findings was thus returned from *Nature* "in case [you prefer] to submit it for early publication to another periodical" [4].

And manifold other examples of the reject errors could be quoted. Although, in hindsight, they cast an aura of stupidity around rejecting editors, such errors nevertheless do not lead to scandals. This is instead the case for the accept errors.

The accept error

In the same way that an experiment could be quoted in relation to reject errors, there is also an example for accept errors. This is the submission in the 1990s of a paper by the physicist Alan Sokal to the journal *Social Text* [5], where he provided a parody of modern cultural studies. After the article had been published, Sokal in a subsequent paper [6] revealed his experiment and phrased his hypothesis in the following way:

> "*Would a leading North American journal of cultural studies [...] publish an article liberally salted with nonsense if (a) it sounded good and (b) it flattered the editor's ideological preconceptions?*"

Needless to say, the Sokal experiment caused embarrassment among post-modern scholars and led to a lot of discussions, which Sokal has summarized in the book *Beyond the Hoax* [7]. However, there are also a number of examples of real scientific frauds. Some 30 years ago, the two science journalists William Broad and Nicholas Wade even started out their book *Betrayers of the Truth* [8] by pointing to fraudulent behaviour among historically recognized scientists such as Ptolemaios, Galilei, Newton, Dalton and Mendel. They also provided information about a number of modern scientific frauds. One of them is Elias A.K. Alsabati, who systematically published already published articles in lesser-known journals [9]. Others include various manipulations of data by the researchers themselves, but also cases where doctoral students manipulated data in order to please their professors (see Chapter 8 in [8]).

As the book by Broad and Wade [8] was published some 30 years ago, it might be argued that the system has become more professionalized and that such fraudulent behaviour is no longer possible. This is not the case, however. Several more recent examples can be mentioned. One of them is the Norwegian oral cancer researcher Jon Sudbø, who managed to publish articles in three prestigious journals, with current impact factors around 50, 18 and 30 respectively, based on manipulated data: *The New England Journal of Medicine* in 2004 [10], *The Journal of Clinical Oncology* in 2005 [11] and *The Lancet* in 2005 [12]. He was exposed and the above-mentioned and several other publications by him were retracted [13].

Another more recent scientific swindler, who has attracted considerable attention, is Woo-Suk Hwang, a professor at Seoul University involved in stem cell research [14]. He and his group even published two articles on cloning in *Science* in 2004 and 2005 [15,16]. However, as early as the fall of 2005 fraudulent behaviour was detected, and the two articles were withdrawn in January 2006 [17].

Nevertheless, in April 2013 the two papers scored 723 and 437 citations respectively on Google Scholar [18].

A third modern example, mentioned in Chapter 4 by Jane Grimson, is Andrew Wakefield, who claimed there was a relationship between vaccination for measles, mumps and rubella, and the appearance of autism and bowel disease. This was based on research results that had been published in *The Lancet* in 1998 [19] and in several other journals. After a long process, where the science journalist Brian Deer played a significant role, the article in *The Lancet* and also those in other journals were retracted [20].

Two very recent examples are provided by the evolutionary biologist Marc Hauser at Harvard University and the Dutch social psychologist Diederik Stapel at Tilburg University. Hauser was considered as a leader in animal cognition research and had among his publications a widely cited article in *Science* (2584 citations on Google Scholar in April 2013), co-authored with the renowned linguist Noam Chomsky and the evolutionary biologist W. Tecumseh Fitch [21]. However, after an investigation that started in 2007 several of his papers were questioned. Hauser was found guilty of scientific misconduct, and among his papers one published in 2002 in *Cognition* (impact factor 3.162) [22] was retracted [23]. Among those following the case was one of the authors of *Betrayers of the Truth* [8], Nicholas Wade [24].

In the case of Diederik Stapel, whistleblowing from some of his students led to the setting up of three committees to investigate his research [25]. They found instances of fraud in some 50 publications, among them dissertations that he had supervised, but also a large number of published articles. Once again, among the fraudulent publications, was a paper published recently in *Science* [26], eventually retracted by Stapel after the committee reports [27]. Most of the rest of the papers were published in the *Journal of Experimental Social Psychology* (impact factor of 2.202), *British Journal of Social Psychology* (impact factor of 1.987) and *European Journal of Social Psychology* (impact factor of 1.592) (see Appendix 4–6 in [25], and [28]). From the first of these journals, published by the American Psychological Association, 14 of the papers were withdrawn after the committee reports [29].

The above may give the impression that scientific fraud is limited to medicine and psychology. This is not the case. One spectacular case is Jan Hendrik Schön from Germany, who rose to prominence through his works on semi-conductors at Bell Labs at the turn of the present century [30,31]. His findings, that transistors could be produced on a molecular scale, attracted wide attention. Again, prestige journals *Nature* and *Science* published papers that were fraudulent. More and more scholars in the field started questioning Schön's findings and a committee found a large number of cases of scientific misconduct [32]. As a result, several papers published in *Nature*, *Science*, *Physical Review* and *Applied Physical Letters* were withdrawn (see e.g. [33–36]).

It could be argued that the above examples of fraudulent behaviour are just a small group of misbehaving individuals. However, a recent systematic review of 2047 biomedical and life-science research articles that had been retracted up to May 2012 reveals that 67.4% of the retractions were attributed to misconduct [37]. The peer-review system thus failed also in a considerable number of other cases.

Errors, impact and reviewers

Errors and impact

The above examples certainly provide evidence that the fraudulent behaviour reported by William Broad and Nicholas Wade in the early 1980s [8] can be found also in subsequent decades. This is particularly worrying, since, as mentioned in the Introduction, the last quarter of a century or so has entailed a tendency that individuals are evaluated on the basis of their success in publishing in top journals. However, as we have seen above, there are reasons to be cautious in drawing the conclusion that high-impact journals publish high-quality papers. Jon Sudbø and Andrew Wakefield published articles in *The Lancet* (impact factor of 32.280) and Woo-Suk Hwang, Marc Hauser and Diederik Stapel published in *Science* (impact factor of 31.201) [37]. In addition, the *Journal of Experimental Social Psychology* (impact factor of 2.202) published as many as 14 articles by Stapel that later had to be retracted. There are therefore strong reasons to question the large emphasis on impact factors. As pointed out by Per O. Seglen [38], they are inappropriate for use in evaluating research, but are nevertheless widely used, or in the words of Kai Simons [39], misused.

Above, we have thus seen that the review system is far from perfect. This means that impact figures should be handled with much more care than is usually the case. There is no doubt that these figures with three decimals create a false impression of exactitude, which has nothing to do with quality. In addition to the deficiencies in reviewing, with both reject errors and accept errors, there are, as pointed out by Seglen [38], a number of reasons to question the use of impact factors for the evaluation of research. It is well known that editors use all sorts of methods to raise the impact factors of their journals: the publication of review articles, pushing for citations of earlier articles from the journal, privileging longer articles, etc. In addition, it is extremely important to note that distributions of citations are highly skewed: most articles, even in high-impact journals, are only cited a few times, if at all. Furthermore, comparisons across scientific fields are inappropriate since they face different conditions. Nevertheless, impact factors are often used in resource-allocation decisions and evaluations.

As mentioned above, in discussing the relationship between impact and quality, it is easier to find spectacular examples of the accept error. However, it is equally important to consider the reject error in this context. It could even be argued that, owing to reject errors, the most innovative research will be found in journals with low impact factors. The reason for this would be that the high-impact journals will be dominated by the scientific elites. These are more likely to reject innovative papers outside the mainstream. As a result, we could expect that significant papers, after rejections in the top journals, end up in lower-impact journals.

Errors and reviewers

Above, we were able to conclude that errors in the peer-review system also occur today. As a matter of fact, we may even suspect that the probabilities for such errors have increased with the passage of time. First of all, owing to the above-mentioned expansion of the system, and the strong pressure to publish, there has been and will be strong growth in the number of manuscripts that are sent to the scientific journals. Secondly, individual researchers may become less inclined to spend time reviewing manuscripts for their community, efforts for which they are not rewarded when they are assessed. This in turn appears to lead to increasing difficulties for editors in recruiting reviewers, and an increasing tendency for them to reject manuscripts without reviews (desk rejects). And, if they get reviewers, we could expect them to be slower to deliver and less careful when they deliver. Such a development may lead both to reject errors and accept errors due to lack of careful reading of manuscripts.

Some evidence regarding the tendencies described above has been obtained in correspondence with the editors of *Nature* and *The New England Journal of Medicine*, as well as the editors of four management journals.

Nature receives some 12 000 manuscripts a year with an increasing trend from 10 584 in 2008 to 12 552 in 2012. A large proportion, as much as 70–80% of these manuscripts, are rejected without review. For the remaining submissions the editor estimates that approximately 30% of those asked to write a review decline. Those who accept the task return their reviews, which are "mostly excellent [...] within 3 weeks or so" (*Nature* Editor-in-Chief, Philip Campbell, personal communication, May 2013). Nevertheless, the strong pressure on the journal in terms of submissions may of course involve risks for errors.

The New England Journal of Medicine has also experienced an increase in the number of submissions. As a result, the share of the desk rejects has increased from 39% in 2002 to 62% in 2012. Nevertheless, the number of reviews has increased from 3870 in 2002 to 6058 in 2012. In the same period, the turn-around performance has increased considerably: 48% of the reviews were returned after 2 weeks and 78% after 3 weeks in 2002, whereas the corresponding figures in 2012 were 67% and 93% respectively (Assistant to the Editor, *The New England Journal of Medicine*, Pamela Miller, personal communication, May 2013). Again, we can see evidence of an increasing flow of manuscripts and higher shares of desk rejections. In addition, we also see increasing pressures to process the manuscripts under review faster.

The increasing flow of manuscripts is also confirmed by the four editors of management journals (personal communications, February 2013). This, in turn, has implied that for all four, approximately one-third of the manuscripts are desk rejected:

> "*On average, one-third of those submissions will be desk rejected.*" (U.S. editor, personal communication, February 2013)

> "[The percentage of desk reject] *was quite high throughout my tenure (papers falling outside the scope of the journal is one category; but there is a lot of rubbish circulating around the world, and most editors will tell you the same story – submissions from outside Europe and North America too often fall into this category.*" (European editor 1, personal communication, February 2013)

> "*At least 30% – my criterion for desk reject was a paper that I would be annoyed receiving for review myself.*" (European editor 2, personal communication, February 2013)

"This was fairly constant at around 35%. But some years saw an increase. This usually coincided with the Research Assessment Exercise in the U.K. when there would be a flood of mediocre papers to beat the census date (not all papers were poor quality but the majority were). This would take the desk rejection rate up to 39/40%. But these were 'blips' in an otherwise constant 35% rejection rate." (European editor 3, personal communication, February 2013)

The perceived need to desk reject certainly implies considerable power for editors, and this in turn could increase the probability of reject errors.

As the European editor 2 points out, the desk reject is important in order not to annoy reviewers. It is also essential in order to decrease the need for reviewers, since, as mentioned above, it is difficult to get their assistance:

"This number has grown quite strikingly over the years. We use three reviewers per manuscript. About five years ago we would have to ask 3.3 people to get 3 reviewers. Today, that number is very close to 4 requests for three reviewers. I think that academics today are much more inclined to refuse a review than past generations." (U.S. editor, personal communication, February 2013)

"Our problem was reviewers never responding [...] Often I had to contact 6–7 people to get 3, and too often I had to contend with 2 reviewers." (European editor 1, personal communication, February 2013)

"30%, on average one of the three assigned reviewers for each paper would be replaced in the process." (European editor 2, personal communication, February 2013)

"This was my greatest headache. I think I coincided as Editor with a time when academics worldwide were becoming increasingly busy in their own institutions and (voluntary) reviewing came fairly low down the priority list for many. I would estimate that out of every three requests for review, one would always decline, so a minimum of 33% declining to review. Annoyingly, some sat on the paper for a few weeks and said nothing (so I assumed they were reviewing the paper). Then they would contact me and say they had to decline. It was at this point that I widened the pool of reviewers to include some junior (but good) faculty. I would use two senior reviewers and one less senior. The standard 'set' of reviewers would comprise one editorial board member, one external senior specialist in the field and one less senior (often general) reviewer. This worked well both in terms of quality and in terms of getting three good reviews for each paper." (European editor 3, personal communication, February 2013)

And, when the assigned reviewers accept the assignment, they take more time than editors like:

"We ask our reviewers to provide their comments within 30 days. We have, over the years, developed a broad range of mechanisms to ensure that we hold

to this number. The logic is this. If we want to get the best manuscripts we have to ensure that authors get prompt but high quality feedback. So, when a reviewer becomes unresponsive or very late with their review, I encourage my reviewers to go with only two reviews if there is consistency in their opinion on the manuscript. If there is not, I have designated some reviewers to be 'on call'. These tend to be very good reviewers who understand that they will sometimes be asked to render an opinion in an attenuated time frame." (U.S. editor, personal communication, February 2013)

"*Chasing reviewers was cumbersome [...] My experience is that this is getting harder and harder to get people to deliver on time (for us: within 5–6 weeks).*" (European editor 1, personal communication)

"*They were given about six weeks but most took three months.*" (European editor 2, personal communication, February 2013)

"*We would demand a 12-week turnaround, but more often than not you would have to wait around 16 weeks to get three reviews for a paper. There were stunning variations however and the range was quite wide. For example I had two or three papers which had all 3 reviews received in 4 weeks. On the other hand, two or three papers had review times of nearly 20 weeks. I guess 16 weeks would be around the average.*" (European editor 3, personal communication, February 2013)

In the present chapter, we may note that the U.S. editor is pushing harder than his European colleagues. This could even be interpreted as an effort to use turnaround time of manuscripts as an asset for a particular journal. However, speed is not enough; quality is also very important in the reviews, and in this respect, editors appear so far to be fairly content with their reviewers:

"*Quality of reviews is of utmost importance. The associate editors rate the quality of each review on a five point scale, with space for additional comments. If reviewers excel in both quality and timeliness, they will be elevated to the editorial review board. Unlike many journals, thus, [our journal] is a meritocracy built on your skill in reviewing. We also acknowledge our outstanding reviewers at the [...] meetings every year. We have just started to put on seminars [...] on how to write a high-quality review.*" (U.S. editor, personal communication, February 2013)

"*Quality of reviews varies a lot: junior scholars often do a thorough job, while some big names end up on a black list after doing an incredibly poor job, or forgetting about having promised to review [...] At the end of the day, editors end up with a bunch of reliable people who you then bother too much [...] An afterthought: I think people should be rewarded by their home universities for reviewing! This is something that is too often forgotten in the contemporary system, which celebrates publishing.*" (European editor 1, personal communication, February 2013)

"*On the whole, the reviews were good. Very seldom did I have to 'reject' a review because of quality or inappropriate advice (but it did happen). While being good, they were also quite often not in mutual agreement. As editor, I had the privilege of mediating between contradictory reviews without alienating any of them."* (European editor 2, personal communication, February 2013)

"Mostly very good. I would say 80–90% of reviews were of good quality. This was a time when I cleared out some of the less active of the Editorial Board (who tended to hand in pedestrian and descriptive reviews which were of little help to me or the authors). Things got better after that in terms of quality of reviews and it was quite rare to receive a poor quality review." (European editor 3, personal communication, February 2013)

From the above comments it is particularly interesting to note how the U.S. editor mentions how the professional association is strengthening reviewing through acknowledgment and through seminars. In the same spirit, the European editor 1 suggests that "people should be rewarded by their home universities for reviewing."

All in all, the editors of the four management journals are thus fairly content with the reviews they have received, although they agree that, first, there is a need to reject about one-third of the manuscripts themselves due to poor quality, secondly, a considerable share of reviewers decline, and thirdly, those who agree take too much time to deliver. To what extent the review processes have reject errors cannot be determined. So far, the editors in question have not been obliged to face accept errors and retractions.

The examination of scientific output is nowadays not limited to editors and their reviewers, however. As far as plagiarism is concerned, modern information technology facilitates more advanced monitoring. Evidence of this is provided by a number of German politicians who have been found to be plagiarists after their dissertations were run through the program VroniPlag. Among them were the Minister of Defence Karl-Theodor zu Guttenberg, the Minister for Education and Research Annette Schavan, as well as the European Parliament members Georgios Chatzimarkakis and Silvana Koch-Merin [40].

The German cases point to the increasing role of the group of actors labelled above as scrutinizers in the governance of academia. Other examples are provided by the work of the science journalists William Broad, Brian Deer and Nicholas Wade, as mentioned above. However, the most powerful mechanism for detecting scientific fraud is always the critical examination by close colleagues and, as was the case regarding Stapel, students.

Conclusions

The point of departure for the present chapter has been the increasing tendency in various disciplines to outsource quality assessments to journal editors and their reviewers. Far too often it seems that actual reading of submitted material is replaced by counting the number of publications in what are considered to be top journals. And these assessments are based on calculations of impact factors, which in turn are based on citations.

Scholars are taking these shortcuts in evaluations at the same time as many of them complain about the power positions that bibliometrics has attained in the past decades. Against this backdrop the paper has provided the following arguments:

1. Editorial decisions include two errors: the reject error and the accept error. The first type is constituted by the rejection of papers that deserve publication, whereas the second type occurs when bad papers are published.
2. Although it is difficult to determine the extent to which these two types of error occur, a number of examples have been provided to show that they have indeed occurred. In this context, it is particularly worth noting that the scandalous accept error has happened in several prestigious high-impact journals, and that these incidents do not seem to harm their reputation.
3. Under the above-mentioned circumstances, it is apparent that it is far from reliable to use impact factors as measures of quality and even less reliable to use them to assess individual researchers.
4. Journal editors seem to face an increasing flow of manuscripts (particularly during times of research assessments) as well as a resistance from potential reviewers, who, as a result of the strong focus on publishing, prefer to publish more of their own papers instead of doing reviews. In addition, those who accept reviewing assignments take more time for their assessments.
5. Finally, it has been pointed out that modern information technology offers new opportunities to reveal plagiarism.

All of this means that it is now urgent more than ever to critically examine academic studies, and not outsource quality assessments to journal editors and their reviewers. As pointed out by Sydney Brenner [41], "we should remind ourselves that what matters absolutely is the scientific content of a paper and that *nothing will substitute for either knowing it or reading it*" [Author's italics].

References

1. Wallis, W.A. and Robert, H.V. (1956) *Statistics: A New Approach*. Free Press, New York
2. Peters, D.P. and Ceci, S.J. (1982) Peer-review practices of psychological journals: the fate of published articles, submitted again. *Behavioral and Brain Sciences* 5, 187–255
3. Yalow, R.S. (1992) Radioimmunoassay: a probe for fine structure of biologic systems. In *Nobel Lectures, Including Presentation Speeches and Laureates' Biographies 1971–1980* (Lindsten, J.E., ed.), pp. 447–468, World Scientific, Singapore
4. Borrell, B. (2010) Nature rejects Krebs's paper, 1937. In *The Scientist*. 1 March 2010, http://www.the-scientist.com/?articles.view/articleNo/28819/title/Nature-rejects-Krebs-s-paper--1937/
5. Sokal, A. (1996) Transgressing the boundaries: toward a transformative hermeneutics of quantum gravity. *Social Text* 14, 217–252
6. Sokal, A. (1996) A physicist experiments with cultural studies. *Lingua Franca* 6, 62–64
7. Sokal, A. (2008) *Beyond the Hoax: Science, Philosophy and Culture*. Oxford University Press, Oxford

8.   Broad, W. and Wade, N. (1982) *Betrayers of the Truth*. Simon and Schuster, New York

9.   Broad, W.J. (1980) Would-be academician pirates papers: five of his published papers are demonstrable plagiarisms, and more than 55 others are suspect. *Science* **208**, 1438–1440

10. Sudbø, J., Lippman, S.M., Lee, J.J. et al. (2004) The influence of resection an aneuploidy on mortality in oral leukoplakia. *New England Journal of Medicine* **350**, 1405–1413

11. Sudbø, J., Samuelsson, R., Risberg, B. et al. (2005) Risk markers of oral cancer in clinically normal mucosa as an aid in smoking cessation counseling. *Journal of Clinical Oncology* **23**, 1927–1933

12. Sudbø, J., Lee, J.J., Lippman, S.M. et al. (2005) Non-steroidal anti-inflammatory drugs and the risk of oral cancer: a nested case-control study. *The Lancet* **366**, 1359–1366

13. Vastag, B. (2006) Cancer fraud case stuns research community, prompts reflection on peer review process. *Journal of the National Cancer Institute* **98**, 374–376

14. Normile, D. (2009) Hwang convicted but dodges jail; stem cell research has moved on. *Science* **326**, 650–651

15. Hwang, W.S., Ryu, Y.J., Park, J.H. et al. (2004) Evidence of a pluripotent human embryonic stem cell line derived from a cloned blastocyst. *Science* **303**, 1669–1674

16. Hwang, W.S., Roh, S.I., Lee, B.C. et al. (2005) Patient-specific embryonic stem cells derived from human SCNT blastocysts. *Science* **308**, 1777–1783

17. Kennedy, D. (2006) Editorial retraction. *Science* **311**, 335

18. Google Scholar search result: Woo-Suk Hwang. http://scholar.google.se/scholar?hl=sv&q=Woo-Suk+Hwang&btnG= (Accessed April 2013)

19. Wakefield, A.J., Murch, S.H., Anthony, A. et al. (1998) Ileal lymphoid nodular hyperplasia, non-specific colitis, and pervasive developmental disorder in children. *The Lancet* **351**, 637–641

20. Godlee, F., Smith, J. and Marcovitch, H. (2011) Wakefield's article linking MMR vaccine and autism was fraudulent. *British Journal of Medicine* **342**, c7452

21. Hauser, M.D., Chomsky, N. and Fitch, W.T. (2002) The faculty of language: what is it, who has it, and how did it evolve? *Science* **298**, 1569–1579

22. Hauser, M.D., Weiss, D. and Marcus, G. (2002) Rule learning by cotton-top tamarins. *Cognition* **86**, B15–B22

23. Retraction notice. (2010) *Cognition* **117**, 106

24. Shaw, K. (2010), Harvard professor found guilty of scientific fraud. In *Ars Technica*. 23 August 2010, http://arstechnica.com/science/2010/08/harvard-professor-found-guilty-of-scientific-misconduct/ (Accessed April 2013)

25. Levelt Committee, Noort Committee and Drenth Committee (2012) *Flawed Science: The Fraudulent Research Practices of Social Psychologist Diederik Stapel* (Translation of *Falende Wetenschap: De Frauduleuze Onderzoekspraktijken van Social-Psycholoog Diederik Stapel*), Tilburg University, Tilburg

26. Stapel, D.A. and Lindenberg, S. (2011) Coping with chaos: how disordered contexts promote stereotyping and discrimination. *Science* **332**, 251–253

27. Stapel, D.A. and Lindenberg, S. (2011) Retraction. *Science* **332**, 2 December

28. Impact factors of psychology journals. http://psychology.wikia.com/wiki/Impact_factors_of_psychology_journals (Accessed April 2013)

29. Retraction watch. http://retractionwatch.com/?s=stapel (Accessed April 2013)

30. Reich, E.S. (2009) *Plastic Fantastic. How the Biggest Fraud in Physics Shook the Scientific World*. Palgrave Macmillan, New York

31. Goodstein, D. (2010) *On Fact and Fraud: Cautionary Tales from the Frontline of Science*. Princeton University Press, Princeton

32. Beasley, M.R., Datta, S., Kogelnik, H., Kroemer, H. and Monroe, D. (2002) Report of the Investigation Committee on the Possibility of Scientific Misconduct in the Work of Hendrik Schön and Coauthors. The Lucent Technologies Report. Available at: http://www.engineering.utoronto.ca/Assets/AppSci+Digital+Assets/pdf/GradStudents+Ethics/Schoen_Full+Report.pdf

33. Retractions (2003) *Nature* **422**, 92. Also available at: http://www.nature.com/nature/journal/v422/n6927/pdf/nature01463.pdf

34. Bao, Z., Batlogg, B., Berg, S. et al. (2002) Retraction. *Science* **298**, 961. Also available at: http://www.sciencemag.org/content/298/5595/961.2.full

35. Schön, J.H., Kloc, C. and Batlogg, B. (2002) Retraction: universal crossover from band to hopping conduction in molecular organic semiconductors [Phys. Rev. Lett. 86, 3843 (2001)]. *Physical Review Letter* **89**, 289902

36. Errata (2002) *Physical Review B* **66**(24), 15 December 2002 (see also http://journals.aps.org/prb/issues/66/24#sect-errata

37.   Fang, F.C., Steen, R.G. and Casadevall, A. (2012) Misconduct accounts for the majority of retracted scientific publications. *Proceedings of the National Academy of Sciences United States of America* **110**, 17028–17033

38.   Seglen, P.O. (1997) Why the impact factor of journals should not be used for evaluating research. *British Medical Journal* **314**, 498–502

39.   Simons, K. (2008) The misused impact factor. *Science* **322**, 165

40.   http://www.vroniplag.de/ (Accessed April 2013)

41.   Brenner, S. (1995) Loose end. *Current Biology* **5**, 568

PART V: BIBLIOMETRICS IN THE HUMANITIES AND SOCIAL SCIENCES

11

Bibliometrics: use and abuse in the humanities

Milena Žic Fuchs[1]
University of Zagreb, Croatian Academy of Sciences and Arts, Croatia

Quo vadis bibliometrics?

The symposium *Bibliometrics: Use and Abuse in the Review of Research Performance*, held in Stockholm, 23–25 May 2013, fell within the context of an initiative to put an end to the misuse of JIF (journal impact factors), embodied in the San Francisco DORA (Declaration on Research Assessment) [1] instigated in December 2012 at the meeting of the American Society for Cell Biology. Interestingly, just before the start of the Symposium, reactions to DORA appeared in leading journals and news blogs, such as *Nature News Blog* [2], an editorial in *Science* [3], an editorial on research assessment in *The EMBO Journal* [4], an editorial in *Molecular Biology of the Cell* [5] and an editorial in *eLIFE* [6], to name but a few.

In a sense, DORA can be seen as a kind of culmination of decades-long discussions on bibliometrics, their use and abuse. Debates on the JIF also have a history of discussions as evidenced in leading journals as mentioned above, discussions *pro* and *contra* the JIF often mirroring divergent views (cf. e.g. [7]). In principle, the reactions to DORA can be said to support the main intent of the declaration, that is to address the over-reliance on JIFs in research assessment, as well as providing the basis for a change in the current system of research assessment prevalent in the so-called hard sciences.

It is of course impossible to go into the different nuances that the above-mentioned reactions to DORA stress. However, it should be noted that up to a certain point, they present a range of opinions and that they focus on different points of the declaration. One example is the view of the *Nature* [2], which has not signed DORA, and in which Philip Campbell, Editor-in-Chief of *Nature*, stresses that the group's journals had in the past published many critical views on the excessive use of JIFs. He also states the opinion that some statements in DORA are too sweeping, and thus does not merit the full support of DORA.

Although DORA can be seen as a move in the right direction, for if nothing else it has in a strong way initiated once again the big question of how to assess research performance, in order to assess quality and not peripheral indicators, open questions still remain. Would reducing the 'impact' of JIFs in favour of article-level ones be a true improvement in assessing article quality? Or, should the ultimate goal be evaluating research papers on the basis of their scientific merit? The ongoing discussions will, if nothing else, hopefully lay the foundations for a

[1]Email: mzicfuch@ffzg.hr

possible new culture of research assessment, one primarily based on the content of articles, or simply put, one based on reading the papers themselves, as is clearly stated in the background motto of the Stockholm symposium, a citation of the 1991 Nobel Laureate Richard R. Ernst [8]: "Start reading papers instead of merely rating them by counting citations!"

DORA from the point of view of the humanities

One could expect that from a humanities perspective, the San Francisco DORA [1] would be welcomed in a 'holistic' sense. More specifically, it would be welcomed as a turning point which could bring humanities research assessment a step closer to what humanities scholars have been trying to achieve in articulating assessment criteria for the last couple of decades. A number of points from the declaration can be singled out in this respect, but with necessary additional elaborations in order to pinpoint the specific nature of humanities research outputs and how to evaluate them.

Thus, for instance, DORA underlines the following: "the need to assess research on its own might rather than on the basis of the journals in which it is published in" [1]. If this is intended to mean a return to assessing scientific content, a return to peer judgement, then humanities scholars will endorse such a view. On the other hand, if the trend and intention of DORA is to introduce a citation-based metrics for assessing individual articles, then there is little, if any, support to be expected, for a number of reasons. First and foremost, such a metrics could cover only articles that appear in journals in, for instance, Thomson Reuters' WoS (Web of Science) or Scopus. These databases cover the lesser part of the overall scholarly productions of the humanities in Europe. The multitude of articles published in national languages, in so-called national journals, could not be assessed by an article-based metrics, at least not without setting up sophisticated databases for all European languages, and their respective journals covering all the humanities disciplines.

Another point from DORA, one that would without a doubt be endorsed by humanities researchers, is the JIF 'time frame' of (usually) 2 years. Again, from a holistic perspective, the lifespan of research outputs in the humanities is by far longer than in other domains, not rarely extending over decades, and in some disciplines it even encompasses centuries. The time restriction that follows out of the JIF-led metrics mirrors neither the true nature of humanities research nor the weight of research results.

DORA also points to the necessity of considering a wider range of research outputs in research assessment: "for the purpose of research assessment consider the value and impact of all research outputs (including databases and software)" [1]. For the humanities, this is of special importance for the diversity of research outputs, which in many disciplines outnumbers or reflects different priorities in comparison with other domains of research. In the various 'models' of assessing research performance found for the humanities, much of this diversity is unfortunately not taken into consideration, or if it is, then priorities not inherent in different disciplines are postulated by universities' funding bodies or national-level assessment rules and procedures.

Challenges of research assessment in the humanities

The previous section should be seen as only a brief overview that touches upon the complexity and difficulties encountered in research assessment in the humanities based on some points that appear in DORA. During the last couple of decades, we have been witnessing lively discussions on two interlinked issues, namely how to enhance the *visibility* of research outputs in the humanities and how to set up *evaluation systems*, systems that would reflect the specific nature of humanities research with regard to the diversity of outputs and the diversity of languages [9]. These discussions have shown that attempts at evaluating research performance on the basis of databases such as WoS and Scopus are lacking, particularly in the sense that they do not mirror in many cases the true quality and innovation that this research brings. Briefly, the coverage of humanities publications remains limited in WoS [10,11] or Scopus. Figure 1 gives an overall, clear visual insight into the coverage of the humanities and the social sciences in comparison with other domains [12].

Imposing assessment criteria inherent or derived from the above-mentioned databases ignores and, what's more, distorts insights into research achievements and the way they are publicized through specific outputs characteristic of the humanities. Namely, the specific nature of humanities research is in quite a few disciplines primarily reflected through publication of books, monographs and articles in *national languages*. In some disciplines, a key role is played by revised and commentated editions, collections of data, as well as translations as found in, for instance, philosophy, philology, etc. Such publications are not 'covered' by the databases that may be relevant for other domains of research. Sole reliance on them has already, through various evaluation systems

Figure 1

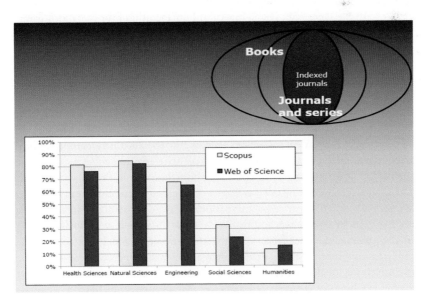

Coverage of Scopus and WoS in different scientific fields

(whether at university level or national level), produced changes in publication cultures in various national research environments throughout Europe. What has been evidenced, for instance, is a more pronounced tendency to publish in English, as shown for the region of Flanders, Belgium, as part of the Flemish performance-based funding system for university research. With respect to the analyses of humanities research outputs in the region of Flanders, Engels et al. [13] show that considerable differences have appeared across the disciplines of the humanities and social sciences in terms of coverage by the WoS. They also indicate a steady increase in the number and proportion of publications in English, with stress on the fact that they vary from discipline to discipline. The so-called English bias attributed to the influential WoS and Scopus is without doubt having impact on language usage in humanities research production, but changes in research agendas have also been noted. Thus within the domain of social sciences, more specifically for economics in Spain, a major shift to international journals indexed in WoS has been noted and analysed, showing that research topics more likely to be received by international journals have become a priority, often replacing local, regional and national topics [14].

Even in the bibliometric literature, one finds 'simplifications' pertaining to the above-mentioned issue of publishing in national languages as well as the audiences that they target. Nederhof [15], for example, identifies three audiences for the social sciences and humanities. First, as in the sciences, publications are directed to other scientists and scholars of the international research frontiers. Secondly, there is a separate audience of regional or national scientists or scholars. Here, use of a regional or national language, as well as regional or national publication media, and a focus on topics thought to be primarily of regional or national interest tend to curtail communication with colleagues elsewhere. Thirdly, there is the non-scholarly audience.

In the same vein, Diana Hicks [16] distinguishes four literatures for the humanities and the social sciences: first, international journals, secondly, national journals, thirdly, books and fourthly, non-scholarly press.

The problem with categorizations such as the above is that they view the humanities (and the social sciences) as in part adhering to the same publishing and outreach patterns most often found in other domains of research, as well as overlooking or glossing over in some cases major differences found in various humanities disciplines especially pertaining to their 'international' and 'national' audiences and subsequent relevance. Namely, the so-called national (or regional) publications directed at national (or regional) scholarly audiences, in disciplines such as literature and linguistics (philology), publications in Dutch, or any of the Slavic languages, to take just two examples of so-called 'small' European languages, are not only read by their respective national or regional scholarly audiences, but are also read by researchers and experts in these disciplines worldwide. Scholars in the philologies, apart from knowing the languages, and being able to read publications written in them, do not often perceive the topics covered as being of exclusively regional or national relevance. Talking to scholars in Dutch or Slavic studies in China, for example, one perceives that what might be 'seen' as a national publication, from their point of view, has a much wider relevance and an obviously wider reading public. The reverse also holds true: sinologists in Europe 'read', and cite for their research, publications in Chinese, and this of course applies to all scholars doing research on 'national philologies'.

It should also be noted that because of the so-called English bias, often impressive internationally first-ranking research traditions with outputs in French, German, Italian, Spanish, etc., are 'overlooked'. In fact, we come across the phenomenon of English single-language authors who seem to be unaware of the huge body of knowledge within their own fields, for simple linguistic reasons.

The above indicates that a kind of 'relativity of concepts' exists as far as the distinction between what is 'international' and what is 'national' is concerned. It also shows that various disciplines in the humanities adhere to different publication practices, and different outreach, out of which subsequently follows that they may well have different types of 'impact', especially at the so-called international level. These practices do not mean that a bigger push for internationalization in the humanities is not welcome or should not be encouraged. In principle, this should be supported, but it should not be the sole criterion in research assessment, and what is 'international' should be more carefully and precisely defined.

Different disciplines also manifest different priorities in publication outputs: some lean more towards articles, whereas others consider monographs or books to be of the first priority. This brief overview of only some of the characteristics we find in various humanities disciplines confirm Henk Moed's [17] claim that it does not make much sense to make statements about characteristics of the humanities and the social sciences as a whole. The present chapter also supports his view that much more research is needed in order to truly understand the complexities involved.

To make the whole 'assessment landscape' in the humanities even more complex, we are now faced with the advent of the so-called digital humanities, a new emerging area not only of research itself, or providing data for research, but also a new medium for 'publishing' research results, in formats that are a far cry from what is understood by traditional outputs. In June 2013, early-career researchers from the humanities met in Paris to discuss the issues involved in new 'publication' cultures emerging within the sphere of digital humanities. The result of this meeting is a manifesto entitled 'Young Researchers in Digital Humanities: A Manifesto' [18], a document which is an explicit appeal for new digital media, showcasing research and research results, to be included and properly evaluated in assessments for jobs, promotions, research funding, etc. It is hoped that new research outputs that come under this rubric will gain recognition, and they are very much in line with the already mentioned quote from DORA [1], "for the purpose of research assessment consider the value and impact of all research outputs (including databases and software)."

And last but not least, the issue of publishing research results which are outcomes of interdisciplinary research endeavours should at least be mentioned. With the advent of Horizon 2020, The Framework Programme for Research and Innovation (2014–2020), inter/multi/transdisciplinary research will become the focal point of all of the seven Grand Challenges (Societal Challenges as they are now called) envisaged in the documents that form the backbone of this new European funding programme. Inter/multi/transdisciplinarity is inherent in the Grand Challenges, as well as in the 'focus areas' they cover, whether it be personalized medicine, sustainable food security, energy efficiency, water innovation or climate change. Active participation of humanities and social sciences scholars is a must if answers to the Grand Challenges are to be found and the 'focus areas' challenges are to be met. The in-depth intermeshing of scholars from all domains of research should result in new 'cultures of research'. *Mainstreaming* is the term most often used to indicate these new trends, and the fact that the role of the humanities and the social sciences should have their rightful place, and not simply be 'icing on the cake'. Fully fledged engagement of the humanities and the social sciences should be implemented from start to finish.

In preparation for more integrated approaches to interdisciplinarity, the ESF (European Science Foundation) organized, in the summer of 2012, an event for early-career researchers entitled 'Interdisciplinary Junior Summit, Water: Unite and Divide. Interdisciplinary approaches for a sustainable future' [19]. The event was instigated by the Standing Committee for the Humanities of the ESF, and became a joint effort together with the Standing Committees for Life, Earth and Environmental Sciences, Physical and Engineering Sciences, and the Social Sciences. Without going into details of the event itself, this was an event that brought together 36 young researchers from different domains of science (from all over Europe), and a special issue portraying the Junior Summit on Water was published in JWARP (*Journal of Water Resource and Protection*), an international peer-reviewed open access journal [20]. This issue reflects the enthusiasm and synergy that resulted from the event itself.

However, the young researchers, although impressed by the potentials of interdisciplinary research (for most of them a completely new experience), expressed concerns as to where they could publish results from such research, and what is more, they expressed fears that interdisciplinarity implies publishing in journals with low impact factors. Needless to say, these concerns were directly related to possible negative effects on promotions and job applications. Thus an important 'Grand Challenge' for future models of research performance assessment will be how to evaluate interdisciplinary articles as well as other outputs, whose number can be expected to grow within the context of Horizon 2020. It would indeed be a huge drawback if the kind of metrics dominant at present were to block the possible innovative results of this kind of research, and this does not only pertain to the humanities and social sciences, but to all domains of research.

Research performance assessment in the humanities: how to deal with the challenges

The preceding sections have tried to outline, at least in broad strokes, the diversity we find in humanities research: diversity of outputs, languages and research traditions. Within such a context, it is truly difficult to set up research assessment models, and debates on how to do this have been going on for quite some time. These debates often mirror opposed views between, on the one hand, different humanities research communities throughout Europe, and on the other, funders and evaluation committees. Opposing perspectives can be summed up, at least in rough terms, into major approaches to research assessment. Thus we encounter a strong voice that is against any kind of 'bibliometric evaluation', and strongly advocates reliance on peer judgements as the basis of research assessment. Conversely, equally strong arguments can be heard for taking humanities to a higher, more formalized, 'bibliometric level'.

These opposed views are also especially visible when we view reactions to the ERIH (European Reference Index for the Humanities), launched in 2001 by the Standing Committee for the Humanities of the ESF. Although the main aim of ERIH was from its very beginnings to enhance *global visibility* of high-quality research in the humanities published in academic journals in various European languages across all of Europe, in some circles, it was initially perceived as a ranking mechanism, hence an evaluation tool. What is more, in some countries, it actually was used for assessing research performance after the so-called Initial Lists were published in 2007 and 2008. The use of ERIH as an 'evaluation tool' primarily lies in the categorization of journals into A, B and C according to the following 'definitions' in shorthand:

- Category A: high-ranking international journals with high visibility that are regularly cited all over the world.
- Category B: standard international journals with significant visibility and influence.
- Category C: high-ranking national or regional journals with recognized scholarly significance.

The ERIH Steering Committee, as well as the Standing Committee for the Humanities, considered feedback on the A, B and C category names, often perceived as a *ranking*, and in order to avoid further misuses introduced new category names as well as giving *national journals* major prominence.

- National journals (or NAT): European publications with a recognized scholarly significance among researchers in the respective research domains in a particular (mostly linguistically circumscribed) readership in Europe.
- International journals (or INT1 and INT2): both European and non-European publications with an internationally recognized scholarly significance among researchers in the respective research domains, and which are regularly cited worldwide.

The revised ERIH lists, with new category names, were published in 2011 and 2012 and were preceded by the following warning [21]:

> "*More specifically it is not intended as bibliometric information for use in assessment processes of individual candidates, be it for positions, promotions, research grant awards, etc.*"

Nevertheless, misuses and the abuse of ERIH, especially in national evaluation systems, have persisted in the sense of the two international categories (INT1 and INT2) having been more highly valued than the national category. Thus articles published in national languages were deemed of lesser importance and value, and a strong English-language bias was enforced in direct opposition to the main aim and intent of ERIH as a visibility tool for humanities research in Europe. With the winding down of the ESF (planned for the end of 2015) the main concern of the Science Review Group for the Humanities (the successor of the Standing Committee) is to ensure that ERIH remains a visibility mechanism for humanities research in the future.

During the last decade or so, a growing awareness of the importance of monographs and books, as well as chapters in volumes has even been recognized by the big commercial databases primarily used in research performance assessments. However, the main inclination, as is the case with journals, is to include books published by leading publishing houses worldwide and in principle this again means that we are faced with a strong English-language bias. As stated above, the inclusion of books, monographs, revised edition, collections of data, etc. must be included in the evaluation of research performance in the humanities. This issue should be addressed at both the national level as well as at the European level, and possibly in the future the importance of books may well reappear in the research assessment of other domains of research. In this respect, it is worth quoting the following from an editorial entitled 'Back to Books' published in *Nature* in 2010 [22]:

> *"The expansiveness of a book allows sophisticated arguments to be put forward and widely debated; new ideas that cross disciplinary boundaries can more readily be shared and worked through.*
>
> *But if this exhortation is to have any traction, the effort and skill required to write a book needs to be rewarded in the career recognition of scientists who devote time to mastering the art to good effect, a recognition that is commonplace in the social sciences and humanities. It is time to bring the book back to the science mainstream."*

At present in Europe there are a number of endeavours aiming at solving the national language issue or challenge with respect to the diversity of research outputs in the humanities. Two stellar examples are, probably the best-known database of this kind, the Norwegian CRIStin (Current Research Information System in Norway) [23,24], as well as the VABB-SHW, a full-coverage database of peer-reviewed publication outputs in the humanities and social sciences developed for the region of Flanders as part of the Flemish performance-based funding system for university research [25,26]. Databases of these kinds can be seen as a way forward in encompassing the full diversity of humanities research outputs, thus providing a healthy foundation for humanities research performance assessment. They also provide, which is of the utmost importance, insights into the changing publication cultures evolving [13].

The above examples are very much in line with what humanities scholars have been insisting on for quite some time, namely the importance of peer judgements. If 'metrics' has to be included in evaluation, then assessment should be *metrics-informed* and not *metrics-led*. The creation of national databases of journals, monographs, and other research outputs is the necessary first step in achieving 'healthy' and quality-oriented research performance assessments in the humanities. The ideal at some point, possibly in the distant future, would be a European-level database encompassing all existing national databases for the humanities and the social sciences found in European research environments. This would ensure that all the types of diversities discussed so far would be reflected both at national and European levels, and it would ensure that the humanities would finally have a research assessment system in line not only with different languages and different outputs, but also with different research traditions in the various disciplines. Such an approach could also ensure ways to account for academic excellence in the true sense of the word and would at the same time provide a basis for transparency in research assessment.

References

1. San Francisco Declaration on Research Assessment (DORA). http://www.ascb.org/SF declaration.html
2. Van Noorden, R. (2013) Scientists join journal editors to fight impact-factor abuse. In *Nature News Blog*. 16 May 2013, http://blogs.nature.com/news/2013/05/scientists-join-journal-editors-to-fight-impact-factor-abuse.html
3. Alberts, B. (2013) Impact factor distortions. *Science* **340**, 787
4. Pulverer, B. (2013) Impact fact-or fiction? *The EMBO Journal* **32**, 1651–1652
5. Bertuzzi, S. and Drubin, D.G. (2013) No shortcuts for research assessment. *Molecular Biology of the Cell* **24**, 1505–1506
6. Schekman, R. and Patterson, M. (2013) Science policy: reforming research assessment. *eLIFE* **2**, e00855
7. How to improve the use of metrics (2010) *Nature* **465**, 870–872
8. Ernst, R.R. (2010) The follies of citation indices and academic ranking lists. *CHIMIA International Journal for Chemistry* **64**, 90
9. Žic Fuchs, M. (2011) Humanities and social sciences at a crossroads? The bibliographic/bibliometric divide. ECOOM Colloquium: assessing research performance in the social sciences and humanities. https://www.ecoom.be/sites/ecoom.be/files/downloads/4%20Milena%20Zic%20Fuchs.pdf
10. Adams, J. and Tesla, J. (2011) Thomson Reuters Book Citation Index. The 13th Conference of the International Society for Scientometrics and Informatic, Durban, South Africa (Noyons, E., Ngulube, P. and Leta, J., eds), pp. 13–18, ISSI, Leiden University and University of Zululand
11. Archambault, E., Vignola-Gagne, E., Cole, G., Larivière, V. and Gingras, Y. (2006) Benchmarking scientific output in the social sciences and humanities: the limits of existing databases. *Scientometrics* **68**, 329–342
12. Sivertsen, G. (2011) Achieving complete and comparable data and output indicators for scholarly publishing in the humanities and social sciences. http://bibliometrie.univie.ac.at/fileadmin/user_upload/ub_bibliometrie/sivertsen.pdf
13. Engels, T.C.E., Ossenblok, T.L.B. and Spruyt, E.H.J. (2012) Changing publication patterns in the social sciences and humanities. *Scientometrics* **93**, 373–390
14. Carmona, S., García-Ferrer, A. and Poncela, P. (2005) From zero to infinity: the use of impact factors in the evaluations of economic research in Spain. *IE Working Paper*, WP05-22, 13-05-2005
15. Nederhof, A.J. (2006) Bibliometric monitoring of research performance in the social sciences and the humanities: a review. *Scientometrics* **66**, 81–100
16. Hicks, D. (2004) The four literatures of social science. In *Handbook of Quantitative Science and Technology Research* (Moed, H.F., Glänzel, W. and Schmoch, U., eds), Kluwer Academic, Dordrecht
17. Moed, H.F. (2011) Research assessment in social sciences and humanities. ECOOM Colloquium: assessing research performance in the social sciences and humanities, https://www.ecoom.be/sites/ecoom.be/files/downloads/1%20Lecture%20Moed%20Ecoom%20Antwerp%209%20Dec%202011%20SSH%20aangepast%20%282%29.pdf
18. Young researchers in digital humanities: a manifesto. https://docs.google.com/document/d/1rk1nfSqG5qqOoNSs9Q-LC3Km8glfaBP_tC4Q79-hT6E/edit?usp=sharing

19. Interdisciplinary Junior Summit, Water: Unite and Divide. Interdisciplinary approaches for a sustainable future http://www.esf.org/hosting-experts/scientific-review-groups/humanities/strategic-activities/esf-junior-summit.html

20. *Journal of Water Resource and Protection* (JWARP) **5**, No. 4A, http://www.scirp.org/journal/jwarp or http://www.esf.org/water

21. ESF Standing Committee for the Humanities (SCH) foreword. https://www2.esf.org/asp/ERIH/Foreword/index.asp

22. Back to books. (2010) *Nature* **463**, 588

23. Schneider, P. (2009) An outline of the bibliometric indicator used for performance based funding of research institutions in Norway. *European Political Science* **8**, 364–378

24. Sivertsen, G. (2010) A performance indicator based on complete data for the scientific publication output at research institutions. *ISSI Newsletter* **6**, 22–28

25. Verleysen, F.T. and Engels, T. (2012) Historical publications at Flemish universities, 2000–2009. *Journal of Belgian History* **XLII**, 110–143

26. Verleysen, F., Ghesquière, P. and Engels, T. (2014) The objectives, design and selection process of the Flemish Academic Bibliographic Database for the Social Sciences and Humanities (VABB-SHW). In *Bibliometrics: Use and Abuse in the Review of Research Performance* (Blockmans, W., Engwall, L. and Weaire, D., eds), pp. 115–125, Portland Press, London

12

The objectives, design and selection process of the Flemish Academic Bibliographic Database for the Social Sciences and Humanities (VABB-SHW)

Frederik Verleysen*[1], Pol Ghesquière†[2] and Tim Engels‡[3]
*Centre for Research and Development Monitoring (ECOOM), University of Antwerp, Belgium, †Research Coordination of the Social Sciences and Humanities Group, KU Leuven, Belgium, and ‡Department of Research Affairs and Centre for Research and Development Monitoring (ECOOM), University of Antwerp, Belgium

Introduction

The present chapter introduces the goals, design and procedure of the VABB-SHW (Vlaams Academisch Bibliografisch Bestand voor de Sociale en Humane Wetenschappen/Flemish Academic Bibliographic Database for the Social Sciences and Humanities). After briefly sketching the background and history of the systems for university funding in Flanders (Belgium) and other European countries, we discuss the design and procedure of the VABB-SHW itself. By highlighting some major publication patterns in the SSH (social sciences and humanities) as reflected by the data contained in the VABB-SHW, we thereafter illustrate how the Flemish database is adapted to, and further evolving towards, reliably capturing the diverse publication output of the SSH as practised at Flemish universities. Finally, focusing on book publications, we make a comparison with the selection process in the Scandinavian countries.

Over the last two decades, several European countries have developed systems for measuring research performance in the natural, technical and biomedical sciences, as well as in the social sciences and humanities. In order to improve the quality of research, PRFSs (performance-based research funding systems), with incentive structures linking output 'quality' to funding, have been developed [1]. In the U.K., the RAE (Research Assessment Exercise) (now Research Excellence Framework) has used peer review by disciplinary panels to evaluate the quality of the self-selected top outputs of research units. In Norway, Denmark, Finland and Flanders, a different route was chosen. In these four countries, full coverage bibliographic databases have been developed in order to monitor the academic and scientific production of university scholars. The best-known example of such

[1]Email: frederik.verleysen@uantwerpen.be
[2]Email: pol.ghesquiere@ppw.kuleuven.be
[3]Email: tim.engels@uantwerpen.be

a database is CRIStin (Current Research Information System in Norway), which collects all bibliographic information from universities and university colleges, research institutes and hospitals in Norway [2–4]. Having led the way in Europe, CRIStin shares some important characteristics with the information systems of Finland, Denmark and Flanders: first, the whole peer reviewed publication output is taken into account for calculation of research funding distribution; secondly, both WoS (Web of Science)-indexed and non-WoS publications are taken into account; and thirdly, evaluation is performed foremost at the level of the publication channel instead of that of the individual publication. Besides similarities, there are also differences between these national systems. The major similarities and differences will be addressed in the present chapter.

In Flanders, the Dutch-speaking region of Belgium, the development of a regional PRFS has come a long way. It was first made possible through the devolution of education and research policy from the federal government to the regions in 1988. From the 1990s onwards, regional authorities in Belgium have played a major role in distributing university funding. Having inherited from the federal state a mixed funding model of both input and output parameters [5], the Flemish government gradually developed its own system for university research. Over the years, this system has become more strongly determined by output-parameters, including publications and citations. Funding of Flemish universities is currently based on four pillars: (i) the block grant for academic education, research, scientific and social services, (ii) parallel government financing for basic research [amongst which is included the BOF (Bijzonder Onderzoeksfonds/University Research Fund)], (iii) other financing sources for research (e.g. the European Union), and (iv) third-party financing of university contract research. The BOF, in particular, has provided the Flemish universities with a tool for shaping their own research policies for basic research. In 2013, the BOF accounted for some €140 million, distributed across the five universities. Over the years, the BOF distribution key has become the standard for setting up funding mechanisms. Most modifications or additions were first implemented as one of several revisions of the BOF key and then later implemented in other funding mechanisms as well [6].

Since 2003, the monitoring of the Flemish universities' research publications has come to the forefront in determining the allocation of funding, especially the BOF [7]. As the Flemish government wanted to give the interuniversity allocation of research funding a more competitive character, distribution of means was increasingly determined on the basis of publications and citations. The growing orientation towards performance-based funding intended to reward the quality of the research performed. In order to distribute the BOF yearly, an accurate counting of publications and citations for all disciplines is essential. During the years 2003–2010, the databases for journal articles and conference proceedings comprised in Thomson Reuters' WoS were used for this purpose. The publications by academics working in Flanders indexed in the WoS were counted and used as a proxy for the total academic output. This way of counting was, however, strongly criticized by the scholarly community in Flanders, among other things because it was considered biased towards the natural and biomedical sciences [8]. The WoS has a low coverage of journals for many disciplines within the SSH [9]. In 2008, the Flemish government amended the BOF regulation in order to make possible the construction of a bibliographic database for registration of publications in the SSH, the VABB-SHW. The primary goal of the VABB-SHW is to allow the inclusion of a specific SSH publications parameter (based on SSH publications that are not included in the WoS) in the calculation of the BOF key. Hence, by enacting a legal framework for the VABB-SHW, the government explicitly recognized that publication cultures in the SSH differ greatly from those in the natural and biomedical sciences, amongst other things regarding distribution of publication types, language use and international orientation [10]. In the latest revision of the BOF regulation [11], the government decided to substantially increase the weight of the VABB-SHW from 2.7 to 6.28% of the BOF key in 2013 [6], thus recognizing the importance of the database.

In the next section, we will have a further look at the design of and the decision-making underpinning the VABB-SHW. This is followed by an overview of some publication patterns in Flemish SSH research as reflected by the contents of the third VABB-SHW. To conclude, we contrast some of these results with the situation in the Nordic countries and offer reflections on the selection process for publications in the various countries.

Design and procedure of the VABB-SHW

The VABB-SHW collects all bibliographic references since the year 2000 of SSH publications by scholars affiliated with a Flemish university. In accordance with the stipulations of the BOF regulation, the following five publication types are eligible for inclusion in the VABB-SHW:

- Articles in journals
- Monographs
- Edited books
- Articles or chapters in books
- Proceedings papers that are not part of special issues of journals or of edited books

The BOF regulation further lists a number of basic criteria which outputs eligible for inclusion need to meet:

- Be publicly accessible
- Be unambiguously identifiable by an ISBN or an ISSN number
- Make a contribution to the development of new insights or to applications resulting from these insights
- Have been subjected, prior to publication, to a demonstrable peer-review process by scholars who are experts in the (sub)field to which the publication belongs. Peer review should be carried out by an editorial board, a permanent reading committee, external referees or by a combination of these. The review should contain input from outside the author(s)'s research team and should be independent from the author(s). The author cannot organize the peer review of her or his own draft manuscript

Finally, the BOF regulation mentions the relative weight each publication type is to receive in the calculation of the BOF key:

- Journal article: 1
- Monograph: 4
- Book chapter: 1
- Edited book: 1
- Conference proceeding: 0.5

The Flemish government decided to entrust the co-ordination and technical construction of the VABB-SHW to the Antwerp branch of the inter-university ECOOM (Expertisecentrum Onderzoek en Ontwikkelingsmonitoring/ Centre for Research and Development Monitoring). Annually, the five Flemish universities provide ECOOM-Antwerp with bibliographic information of the SSH publications by their researchers that appeared in the previous 2 years. In order to safeguard the academic standards of the VABB-SHW, the Flemish government simultaneously decided to establish a GP (Gezaghebbend Panel/ Authoritative Panel), which is composed of 18 professors affiliated with Flemish universities and whose expertise covers the main SSH disciplines. It is the task of the GP, assisted by disciplinary panels, to evaluate which of the journals and book publishers (with whom researchers affiliated with a Flemish university have published at least once in the retrospective 10-year sliding time window used for the BOF key) meet the aforementioned criteria. In accordance with the BOF regulation, WoS-indexed articles, letters, proceedings papers and reviews, as well as their citations automatically contribute to the calculation of the BOF key. One extra criterion for individual publications eligible for inclusion was introduced by the GP: they must be at least four pages long.

In the VABB-SHW, all records are assigned to 16 SSH disciplines and/ or one of three general categories on the basis of the author(s)' affiliation(s) with a SSH unit, i.e. the research group, the research centre, the institute or the department in which the author carries out research. This uniform and complete attribution of publications to disciplines allows ECOOM to annually provide the GP with overviews of all publication channels used by researchers affiliated with the Flemish universities. The overviews of journals, book publishers, book titles and proceedings papers are thus provided for the database as a whole and per discipline, thereby facilitating the work of the GP and its disciplinary subpanels. The work of the GP results in separate lists of approved and non-approved publication channels. The GP's judgement is thereafter applied by ECOOM-Antwerp to all individual publications submitted by the universities. The updated version of the VABB-SHW is delivered to the government on 30 June each year, allowing for timely calculation of the BOF key for the following year. The final lists of approved publication channels are made available through the ECOOM website (http://www.ecoom.be/en/vabb). Figure 1 shows the annual cycle for updating VABB-SHW.

Figure 2 presents the approval rate of the articles and book publications submitted for inclusion in the VABB-SHW. The approval rates represent the percentage of the articles and book publications, published in a certain year

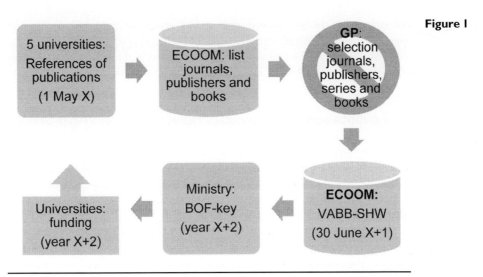

Figure 1

Yearly cycle for updating the **VABB-SHW** and calculation of the **BOF key**

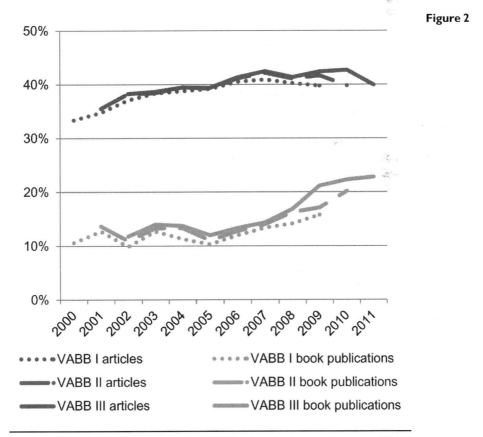

Figure 2

• • • • •VABB I articles   • • • • •VABB I book publications

━━•VABB II articles   ━━•VABB II book publications

━━VABB III articles   ━━VABB III book publications

Approval rates for articles and book publications in the versions one (2010) to three (2012) of the VABB-SHW

and included in the first, second and/or third version of the VABB-SHW. The approval rate for book publications in the VABB-SHW is considerably lower than the approval rate for journal articles. As is discussed in the next section, this has consequences for the share of each publication type within the VABB-SHW.

SSH publication characteristics reflected in the VABB-SHW

The VABB-SHW has succeeded in realizing a more balanced output measurement for the SSH than the previous system which only took into account the WoS-indexed publications. This is apparent from the distribution between the WoS-indexed (VABB-WoS) and the non-WoS, but GP-approved, publications (VABB-GP) included in the database (Figure 3).

For most SSH disciplines, VABB-GP publications outnumber VABB-WoS by a great margin. Only in three social science disciplines, i.e. economics and business, psychology, and social health sciences, does VABB-WoS account for a larger share than VABB-GP (Figure 3). This observation is to be expected, as these disciplines are known to be well covered by the WoS [3,9,12].

This more balanced measurement achieved by the VABB-SHW is also reflected by the distribution of publication languages (Figure 4).

Although English has become the dominant publication language in all but two disciplines, Dutch and other languages still account for a sizeable share of Flemish SSH publication output. This is more so the case for the humanities than for the social sciences. Those SSH disciplines that study more regional topics

Figure 3

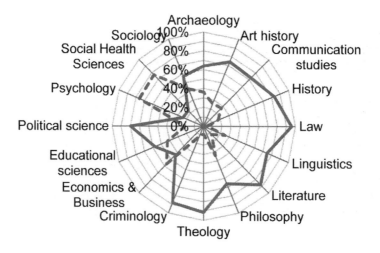

———VABB-GP   ▬ ▬ ▬ VABB-WoS

Shares of VABB-WoS and VABB-GP in the third version of the VABB-SHW

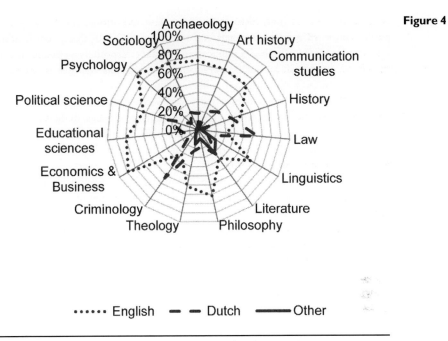

Figure 4

Publication languages in the third version of the **VABB-SHW**

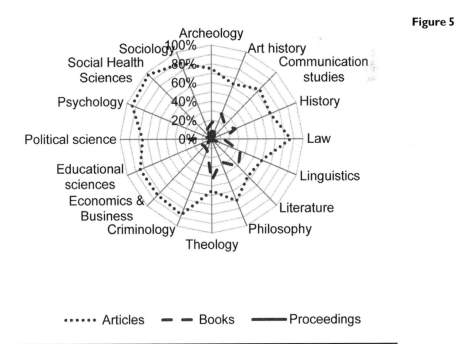

Figure 5

Publication types in the third version of the **VABB-SHW**

(such as political science, history, literature, law and criminology) also seem to publish more in regional journals and with regional publishers, which adhere more frequently to Dutch as a publication language. Especially in the humanities, the choice for Dutch and other publication languages as opposed to English is determined by both research topic and target audience [10].

Above, we pointed out that lower acceptance rates for books have a consequence for the distribution of the various publication types. In the VABB-SHW (third version, 2012), journal articles account for 69.2%, book publications (monographs, edited books and chapters together) account for 28.6% and conference proceedings account for 2.2% (Figure 5).

Despite the dominance of the journal article, book publications represent a considerable share in most disciplines, especially in the humanities. Yet, the distribution between publication types for the VABB-SHW differs substantially from the one in the comparable Norwegian CRIStin database. There, book publications account for 50.8% in the social sciences and for 61.0% in the humanities [3,13]. How is such a large difference in the share of book publications possible? As trends in journal publication patterns of SSH scholars in Flanders and Norway have been shown to be rather similar [12], difference in publication cultures is not a sufficient explanation. Part of the explanation can be found in the different selection process for book publications in both countries. We discuss these procedural differences and the resulting decisions in the next section.

VABB-SHW book publisher selection compared with Denmark, Finland and Norway

For each version of the VABB-SHW, the main task of the GP is to evaluate which publication channels (journals and publishers) meet the criteria stipulated in the BOF regulation. For book publishers, the selection for the first version of the VABB-SHW was based on the level-2 list of top-rated international scientific publishers who (i) target a mainly scientific readership, (ii) apply rigorous external peer review, (iii) publish in the major language(s) of each discipline, and (iv) attract an international authorship with no more than two-thirds of the authors coming from one and the same country. This list had been identified in an earlier similar exercise for the construction of CRIStin in Norway. This level-2 list also served as the basis of the publisher selection in Denmark and Finland. In Norway and Finland, the level-2 list was supplemented by more sizeable level-1 lists, containing many other publishers for which authors declared that peer review of their own publications with these publishers had taken place. Level-1 list publications are also included in the national bibliographic databases of Norway and Finland. Yet, for the calculation of research funding in the Nordic PRFSs they carry less weight than the level-2 publications (e.g. 5 publication points as opposed to 8 for level-2 monographs in Norway) [2]. Denmark uses no level distinctions for publishers, but groups all publishers in one list. By contrast, in Flanders, the GP decided that only the Norwegian level-2 list of 82 publishers would serve as the initial basis of the publisher selection for the VABB-SHW, and that no level-1 list would be added. The GP concurred, however, that at a later stage the VABB-SHW publisher list would be expandable [14]. Consequently, the list of approved publishers has grown for the subsequent versions of the VABB-SHW: three publishers were added in 2011, 33 in 2012 and another 23 in 2013.

In addition to the continuing expansion of the list of approved publishers, from the second version of the VABB-SHW onwards, arrangements have been made by the GP for the inclusion of a selection of individual book publications that meet the criteria of the BOF regulation. Starting in 2010, a quality label for peer-reviewed books was created by the VUV (Flemish Publishers' Association). This GPRC (Guaranteed Peer Reviewed Content) label can be attached to individual books pending GP approval, which thus are also included in the VABB-SHW [15]. In addition, the GP decided to screen recent book publications in order to be able to identify foreign published records that meet the BOF criteria. Moreover, starting in 2013, peer-reviewed series of books have been included as well. These more fine-grained selection processes for book publications allow the VABB-SHW to capture the peer-reviewed research outputs published by scholars affiliated with the Flemish universities more and more reliably. Moreover, an appeals procedure yearly allows authors of publications that have not been accepted for inclusion in the VABB-SHW to prove that peer review has actually taken place, leading the GP to revise their decision so that the publication can be included in the next version of the VABB-SHW.

Let us now return to the difference in share of book publications in the VABB-SHW and CRIStin respectively. The primary cause for this divergence seems to be the difference in selection mechanism. Whereas in Flanders, decision-making is centralized with the GP, in Norway, it is the researchers and their departments who have to indicate whether a publication has been the subject of peer review prior to publication. Only when this is contested is discussion at a more distant, i.e. more centralized, level to take place. Yet, it may also occur that publishers are judged differently in Flanders as compared with Denmark, Finland and/or Norway.

To analyse the occurrence of diverging judgement at the publisher level, we examined the occurrence on the Nordic level-2 and level-1 lists of the 118 approved and the 1747 non-approved publishers that occur in the VABB-SHW database (third version, 2012). For now, such a publisher matching is only possible at the level of publisher names, as only in Flanders algorithmically derived ISBN prefixes are uniformly implemented as a unique publisher ID.

The result of this matching can be grouped in four categories:

(a) Publishers approved in Flanders, as well as in the Nordic countries
(b) Publishers approved in Flanders, but not occurring on the list of approved publishers in any of the Nordic countries
(c) Publishers approved in the Nordic countries, but not approved in Flanders
(d) Publishers with a different approval result in at least two of the four countries

Starting with category (a), the large majority of the publishers approved in Flanders occur on the lists of approved publishers in the Nordic countries as well. The percentage to be found on the Danish publisher list is 83.0%, with 86.1% for the Finish list and 86.8% for the Norwegian list. In the case of Finland and

Norway, most of the publishers approved in Flanders are actually on level 2 (65.9 and 61.2% respectively).

In category (b), six publishers were found to be approved in Flanders, but not in the Nordic countries. In category (c), 188 publishers (10.8% of 1747) are not approved in Flanders, but are approved in Denmark (no levels) and approved at level 1 in Finland and Norway. Nineteen publishers not approved in Flanders (1.1% of 1747) are approved at level 2 in Finland and/or Norway. For some of these publishers, the GP has identified peer-reviewed book series or individual books that have been peer reviewed, but the majority of the book publications with these publishers have not been included in the VABB-SHW for lack of evidence of peer review. Finally, in category (d), six publishers were not approved in Flanders and were judged differently in Norway (level 1) and Finland (level 2). This result illustrates that, in addition to differences in perception regarding the implementation of peer review, differences in the perception of the standing of publishers also occur.

Overall, our analysis illustrates that there is both considerable agreement as well as divergence regarding the inclusion of publishers in the performance-based research funding systems of Denmark, Finland, Flanders and Norway. This illustrates the general agreement on what constitutes the international layer of social sciences and humanities publications, but the lack of such agreement with regard to the publications that are more culturally embedded, focus more on local issues and/or primarily target a national or local audience. The latter publications, however, are an essential part of social sciences and humanities academic output. This illustrates that although the inclusion of book publications in performance-based funding systems is a huge improvement over systems that include articles only, issues remain for SSH scholars [16].

Conclusion

In the present chapter, we have introduced the VABB-SHW database and have compared its book-selection process with that of the performance-based research funding systems that have been implemented in Denmark, Finland and Norway. In each of these countries, recognition of the diverse publication culture of the SSH has resulted in comprehensive-coverage databases of publications that include book publications. Yet, the percentage of book publications differs considerably, with the percentage in Flanders being lower than in the Nordic countries. This illustrates the lack of standardization of peer review of book publications, if applied at all. In fact, many publishers have thoroughly reviewed series, as well as non-reviewed books in their portfolio, and the peer review may concern book proposals or entire manuscripts [15]. Moreover, there is almost no tradition of selecting publications at the publisher level. With the advent of Thomson Reuters' Book Citation Index and the envisioned addition of 75000 books to Elsevier's Scopus database, this situation may be changing. Yet, the diversity of publishers is enormous, especially in the humanities, hence necessitating more fine-grained approaches such as selection at the series and even the individual book level.

Acknowledgements

We thank Gunnar Sivertsen, Karen Skytte Larsen, Rolf Halse and Truyken Ossenblok for their assistance and suggestions.

References

1. Hicks, D. (2012) Performance-based university research funding systems. *Research Policy* **41**, 251–261
2. Schneider, J.W. (2009) An outline of the bibliometric indicator used for performance-based funding of research institutions in Norway. *European Political Science* **8**, 364–378
3. Sivertsen, G. (2009) Publication patterns in all fields. In *Celebrating Scholarly Communication Studies: A Festschrift for Olle Persson at his 60th Birthday* (Aström, F., Danell, R., Larsen, B. and Schneider, J.W. eds). International Society for Scientometrics and Informetrics, Leuven
4. Sivertsen, G. (2010) A performance indicator based on complete data for the scientific publication output at research institutions. *ISSI Newsletter* **6**, 22–28
5. Moed, H.F., Luwel, M., Houben, J.A., Spruyt, E. and Van Den Berghe, H. (1998) The effects of changes in the funding structure of the Flemish universities on their research capacity, productivity and impact during the 1980s and early 1990s. *Scientometrics* **43**, 231–255
6. Spruyt, E.H.J. and Engels, T.C.E. (2013) Nieuwe sleutel verdeling van middelen Bijzonder Onderzoeksfonds. *Thema: Tijdschrift voor Hoger Onderwijs en Management* **13**, 56–61
7. Debackere, K. and Glänzel, W. (2004) Using a bibliometric approach to support research policy making: the case of the Flemish BOF-key. *Scientometrics* **59**, 253–276
8. De Wever, B. (2007) Van A1, A2, A3... Concurrentievervalsing in academia. In *Welke Universiteit Willen Wij (Niet)?* (Loobuyck, P., Vanheeswijck, G., Van Herck, W., Grieten, E. and Vercauteren, K., eds), Academia Press, Gent
9. Archambault, E., Vignola-Gagne, E., Côte, G., Larivière, V. and Gingras, Y. (2006) Benchmarking scientific output in the social sciences and humanities: the limits of existing databases. *Scientometrics* **68**, 329–342
10. Hicks, D. (2004) The four literatures of social science. In *Handbook of Quantitative Science and Technology Research: The Use of Publication and Patent Statistics in Studies of S&T Systems* (Moed, H.F., Glänzel, W. and Schmoch, U., eds), Kluwer Academic, Dordrecht
11. Decision of the Flemish government on the financing of the Special Research Funds at the universities in the Flemish community. http://go.nature.com/mt9srg (In Dutch)
12. Ossenblok, T.L.B., Engels, T.C.E. and Sivertsen, G. (2012) The representation of the social sciences and humanities in the Web of Science. A comparison of publication patterns and incentive structures in Flanders and Norway (2005–9). *Research Evaluation* **21**, 280–290
13. Piro, F.N., Aksnes, D.W. and Rorstad, K. (2013) A macro analysis of productivity differences across fields: challenges in the measurement of scientific publishing. *Journal of the American Society for Information Science and Technology* **64**, 307–320
14. Ghesquière, P., Van Bendegem, J.-P., Gillis, S., Willems, D. and Cornelissen, K. (2011) Het VABB-SHW: eerste versie klaar, nu verfijnen. In *Vlaams Indicatorenboek 2011* (Debackere, K. and Veugelers, R., eds), Expertisecentrum O&O Monitoring, Brussels
15. Verleysen, F.T. and Engels, T.C.E. (2013) A label for peer-reviewed books. *Journal of the American Society for Information Science and Technology* **64**, 428–430
16. Hicks, D. (2013) One size doesn't fit all: on the co-evolution of national evaluation systems and social science publishing. *Confero: Essays on Education, Philosophy and Politics* **1**, 67–90

Acknowledgements

13

The use of indicators in French universities

**Stéphanie Chatelain-Ponroy*[1], Stéphanie Mignot-Gérard†[2],
Christine Musselin‡[3] and Samuel Sponem§[4]**
*Conservatoire National des Arts et Métiers (CNAM), France, †Université Paris-Est
Créteil (UPEC), France, ‡Sciences Po, Centre de Sociologie des Organisation/Centre
National de la Recherche Scientifique (CNRS), France, and §HEC Montreal, Canada

Although the use of bibliometrics is still very limited, or limited to some disciplines [1], the use of indicators in the management of French universities is becoming more and more prevalent and advanced, at least as far as HSS (humanities and social sciences) are concerned [2]. In the present chapter, we will provide evidence of the general use of indicators and of differences between disciplinary fields. In order to put these results in context, we will first provide some information on the French system and how the recent reforms favoured the development of indicators. We will then describe what we have learnt from the qualitative study on the attitudes of the humanities and the sciences to indicators. We will then present some lessons drawn from a quantitative study in which we were able to compare universities mainly specialized in humanities with universities mainly specialized in the sciences. In doing so, we will start out by looking at the use of indicators. This issue has been largely studied in the management sciences, and different authors have suggested different uses. Simons [3] for instance distinguished between diagnostic use of indicators (indicators are used to produce an evaluation of performance) and interactive use of indicators (indicators are used to reveal strengths and weaknesses and to learn about them). Cavalluzzo and Ittner [4] also distinguish between reporting (i.e. providing information about activities), and steering or making decisions (using indicators in order to introduce change).

Drawing on these two typologies, we first look at cases where indicators are used to legitimize what has been done and to account for it. Indicators are produced in order to show that a level of performance is achieved, to provide data required by external actors, describing current achievements. We will also consider cases where data are produced in order to compare units or teams and thus to evaluate their activity. Finally, we look at cases where data and indicators are used in order to make decisions or choices and to take action. The legitimation, evaluation, discussion and decision uses of indicators will be studied for data on teaching, on research and on budgets in order to see whether different issues lead to different uses.

A second issue addressed by the present chapter deals with disciplinary differences. In France, there are some 'complete universities' (with or without medicine), but also many universities specialized in law and economic sciences,

[1]Email: stephanie.chatelain@cnam.fr
[2]Email: stephanie.mignot-gerard@u-pec.fr
[3]Email: christine.musselin@sciencespo.fr
[4]Email: samuel.sponem@hec.ca

universities with a strong orientation in the NS (natural sciences), and universities that are specialized in the HSS. This allows us to compare the uses of indicators in the humanities and the science-dominated institutions (HSS institutions and NS institutions) in the following: the former represent approximately 15% of the French universities and the latter 14%.

Recent reforms and their impact on the development of indicators

French contemporary universities are in fact recent

La Sorbonne and many other institutions on French territory were founded in the Middle Ages. So French universities have a long history. However, this is a limited view [5]. Although the French higher education system is indeed ancient, the French university system as we know it today is celebrating only its 40th anniversary. The Faure act, which was passed in 1968, led to the re-creation of French universities in the early 1970s. This was a radical change of almost two centuries of supremacy of the discipline-based *facultés* (faculties) of law, medicine, science and humanities. Universities had been suppressed in 1793 after the French Revolution, leaving the way open to the foundation of more professional schools, some of them now being among the best French *Grandes écoles*, aimed at training a French elite.[5] However, when Napoleon took power, he recreated the *facultés* as parts of a nation-wide university (the Imperial University). Different *facultés* representing each discipline could be located in the same town, but they were not linked one with another. By the end of the 19th Century, the Third Republic recreated a local level called 'universities' in the different cities, but they were administrative rather than academic and collegial structures: the role and prerogatives of the *facultés* were already so well developed that they remained the main institutional structures in terms of decision-making, co-ordination on the French territory and interactions with the ministry. It is thus only in 1968, after student demonstrations, that a new act was passed with the explicit aim of redesigning French universities and weakening the *facultés*. The *facultés* constituting the University of Paris, la Sorbonne, were therefore reorganized into seven new universities, the University of Montpellier into three, etc.[6] They were given new governing bodies and structures, autonomy (even if this was never fully implemented at that time), parity-based councils and a president elected from among the academics.

The conception of a university that was supported by Napoleon was very different from the Humboldtian model that was developed at about the same time in Germany. For Napoleon, the *facultés* were primarily dedicated to

---

[5] *Les Grandes écoles* is a specific group of institutions (cf. the website of the *Conférence des Grandes écoles* http://www.cge.asso.fr/en), the best of which trained the French industrial, administrative and intellectual elites. Most (especially engineering schools, and schools training the administrative and intellectual elites) are public and almost free (like French universities) in terms of fees, whereas the business schools charge high fees and are mostly parts of chambers of commerce and industry. All of the *grandes écoles* are highly selective.
[6] Today, there is a movement to bring together the institutions that split in 1968. Some even merged as the three universities of Strasbourg in 2009 or the three universities of Marseille in 2012.

training and to delivering degrees, rather than research. It is only after the defeat by Germany in 1870 that French decision-makers (like Louis Liard, the director for higher education at the Ministry) tried to import the German system in France, but they largely failed in trying to develop research [6] within the French *facultés*. Many years later, in 1936, the creation of a national research institution called the CNRS (National Centre for Scientific Research) intended to overcome this deficit in research by creating an institution outside the universities. The development since the mid-1960s of research units affiliated both to a university and to the CNRS has progressively transformed French universities into higher education *and* research institutions, even if the national research institutions (the CNRS and those that were created in the 1950s and 1960s) still play a very important role in French research activities and production.

This specific trajectory of French universities is important to remember if one wants to understand the recent reforms. Their main objectives were directly linked to this history and based on the will to modify its development in two ways: first, by strengthening the governance and the autonomy of French universities and secondly, by transforming French universities into central actors in the French higher education and research system.

Two main reforms: the 2006 and the 2007 acts

At the risk of over-simplification, the objectives of the reforms in the early 2000s empowered the university presidents, on the one hand, and weakened the national research institutions, on the other. The latter were especially targeted in the 2006 act, called the LOPRI (Loi d'Orientation pour la Recherche et l'Innovation/Act for Research and Innovation) with the creation of a national research council [ANR (Agence Nationale de la Recherche/The French National Research Agency)] and an agency for the evaluation of research and higher education [AERES (Agence d'Evaluation de la Recherche et de l'Enseignement Supérieur/Evaluation Agency for Research and Higher education)].[7] Before the LOPRI, the national research institutions (but also the Ministry) were acting as research councils and managing calls for proposals. In 2005, these budgets were taken away from them, reinforced and entrusted to the ANR, thus clearly reducing the programmatic role of the CNRS and other national research institutions such as INSERM (Institut National de la Santé et de la Recherche Médicale/French Institute of Health and Medical Research), or the INRA (Institut National de la Recherche Agronomique/French National Institute for Agricultural Research).

The same act centralized the evaluation of training programmes, research units and higher education and research institutions within one agency. Not only did it change the type of experts who were solicited (more international, appointed and not elected, etc.), but it also deprived the national research institutions of a key function: evaluating their research units with the help of national discipline-based committees. The CNRS and other national research institutions were furthermore

---

[7]Recently transformed into a HCERES (Haut conseil pour l'évaluation de la recherche et de l'enseignement supérieur/council for the evaluation of research and higher education) by the ESR act of July 2013.

asked to limit their roles to the functions of managing research resources (through the personnel they were responsible for and the operating budgets they allocated to the research units affiliated to them and to universities). Universities were to become 'research operators', i.e. to be responsible for the definition of their research agenda and become the main places for research.[8]

The 2007 act (called Pécresse act or LRU act, *Loi relative aux libertés et responsabilités des universités*, Act for the freedom and responsibilities of universities) completed these measures by reinforcing the autonomy of French universities and empowering their presidents by giving them more room for decision, by limiting the size of the university council and the possibility of a powerful opposition, or by giving them the power to block hiring decisions. The slow development of French universities into more autonomous and managed institutions, which started in the early 1990s with the introduction of strategic plans and the signing of 4-year contracts between each university and the ministry [5], was thus accelerated. In parallel, the devolution to universities of the management of their payroll (previously managed by the ministry, whereas universities only managed their operating budgets) represented a huge step as they became responsible for their global budgets.

Reforms favouring the development of indicators

The development of universities into autonomous organizations [7–10] that underlies the recent reforms has been one of the main drivers for the development of indicators and auditing in French universities. In the early 1990s, the introduction of the first 4-year strategic plans and contracts already made universities aware of their ignorance about their own activities and led to the creation of new positions or offices in charge of producing the data for this quadrennial exercise.[9] These contracts became more and more accompanied with indicators of past activity and the forthcoming objectives and goals.

This phenomenon was amplified as universities were provided with more autonomy, but were also simultaneously made more accountable, a classic process that Michael Power has analysed in his book *The Audit Society: Rituals of Verification* [11]. The introduction of a new budgetary process in the French public sector in 2002 accentuated further this trend. It implies that each annual budget has to be justified by the objectives set up by each public entity and that their achievement is to be followed by means of indicators.

With the introduction of the AERES in 2006, there were finally changes in the evaluation processes and an increase in the use of indicators. This trend started well before, but was invisible; by the end of the 1990s, the Ministry developed databases of information from the evaluation of the research units. However, these data were not made public and not (at least explicitly) used to make decisions. At

---

[8]This may sound very curious to a non-French reader, but a specificity of the French system is that universities were neither the most prestigious institutions in terms of training (the *Grandes Écoles* are the more prestigious), nor the more prestigious in terms of research (which the national research institutions are).
[9]Every 4 years, each university signs a contract with the Ministry. The institutions have to submit an assessment of their strengths and weaknesses and develop strategic plans for the next 4 (now 5) years. The contract represents around 15% of the university budget (salaries excluded).

the same time, the former agency in charge of evaluating the governance of universities [the CNÉ (Conseil national de l'évaluation des universités/National Council for the Evaluation of Universities)], that was incorporated in the AERES in 2006, itself produced public reports, but this evaluation was disconnected from the process of budget allocation by the Ministry. This dramatically changed after the creation of the AERES: most of the evaluations are translated into grades (A+, A, B or C), and the grades and the reports are accessible on the AERES website. These evaluations are used by the Ministry, which has introduced a performance-based component in the formula for resource allocations to universities. As a result, it became much more important than ever for universities to monitor their activities, their publications and their results, to know how many grants were obtained by their faculty staff, and to develop better insight into student performance and entry into the job markets. Therefore, it was not surprising that, in our survey in 2011, we observed that 86% of the registrars declared that their university has created an internal auditing office, whereas this figure reached only 65% in the survey led by Stéphanie Chatelain-Ponroy and Samuel Sponem [12] 5 years ago.

Availability and use of data in French universities

A first question to raise about the development of databases and indicators in the French system deals with attitudes vis-à-vis quantified information and whether these attitudes are different for academics in HSS vis-à-vis the NS. The interviews conducted with each group revealed rather contrasting conclusions. In this part of the paper we will therefore present the results from interviews with academics in these three fields, undertaken in June 2011. About 100 interviews were carried out by the students of the Master of Sociology of Sciences Po in three French universities, one humanities oriented (UniHSS), the second science oriented (UniScience) and the third complete with medicine (UniMulti) [13]. In the interview guidelines, some questions were dedicated to the use of indicators and how they were perceived.

In the interviews, academics in HSS who were in charge of managing a research unit, a department, a *faculté* or elected to the university councils, were clearly more critical about the development of indicators than the natural scientists. The critique included complaints about the relevance of the data when applied to the HSS, especially when it comes to bibliometric indicators. Two professional associations developed in the 2000s [SLR (Sauvons la recherche/Save Research) and SLU (Sauvons l'université/Save the University)]; they both have websites on which very critical comments on the recent reforms are posted. They were also very active in 2012 after the socialist government came back to power and announced a new university act. They called for the suppression of evaluations and the reduction or suppression of project-based research, but did not succeed.

It is also clear that academics in the humanities and the social sciences first of all were less used to these forms of quantification than natural scientists are and less comfortable with the idea that each contribution should be ranked. But they were also more anxious about the consequences of these developments for their domain and tried to conceive strategies promoting their research. In the words of a Vice President of a UniHSS:

> "We want to make the humanities and social sciences recognized for their potential and specific contributions [...] It is the humanities and the social sciences for themselves, for their social utility as such, not only as a complement for the sciences. We need to valorize this sector of research and promote it."

One of the main fears comes from the dependence they experience vis-à-vis their institution: their dependence increases when their university starts allocating budgets according to performance or making resources dependent on specific results or behaviours, because they lack opportunities to attract other resources. Not being used to getting grants and finding external funding, they looked upon the development of indicators as a threat because it makes their relationships to the university managers much tighter. This tension was especially palpable in the interviews conducted in the multidisciplinary university where academics in the HSS are in direct competition with natural and life scientists. The new managerial norms that were introduced, the new organization of research in this university (into teams and federations of teams) led to rather critical discourses in the HSS, whereas the natural and life scientists, by contrast, rather welcomed the organizations into federations of laboratories and the fact that research performance was taken into account.

This picture should nevertheless be tempered by the university specialized in the HSS, a university known in France for the opposition of its students and academic staff against the reforms. Despite these circumstances, the university managers (the president and his team of vice presidents, most of them members of a leftist union in higher education, and the administrative directors working under the supervision of the registrar) started to develop indicators on the number of study programmes offered and the number of students attending each class, in order to make decisions about closing small classes and even to set a threshold under which classes should be closed. This is, of course, a very hot topic in a university where rare languages are taught and teachers are struggling for students. But the managers succeeded in fixing a norm and defining the specific cases for which it could be set aside. From the beginning, they consulted the deans and asked them to define norms and to set priorities, but also to define the relevant indicators. They favoured the use of common indicators and the use of common data. Thus, even if it is impossible to draw general conclusions from this case, it seems that the reluctance of the HSS to using indicators is linked to how this policy is implemented and the extent to which indicators are adapted to these two fields.

Availability and use of data in French universities

In addition to the above-presented interviews we undertook a survey of all French universities between May and September 2011. The sample addressed the presidential team (presidents and vice presidents), the directors of the university administration and the registrar, the administrative and academic elected members of the deliberative bodies (university council, academic councils and council for student affairs) of universities, the deans, heads of departments and directors of laboratories, as well as their administrative counterparts. We received approximately 2600 answers (total response rate, 22%; for HHS institutions, 16%; for NS institutions, 18%). A report was written on the results of this survey [14]. Part of the survey concerned indicators and the use of indicators.

In view of the increase in information and data produced by universities and the increasing role of indicators in the French higher education system, the survey included a large set of questions on the available data. We more specifically tried to see what data were available and what they were used for when they became available. In this part of the chapter, we only consider the disciplinary orientation of the institution of the informant. Their answers will be compared with those of the total sample (all universities, i.e. the results for all the universities that participated to the study), including universities oriented towards the HSS, as well as NS universities.

Available data in both groups of institutions

First looking at data that relate to teaching, Table 1 provides the average answers for all French institutions and for HSS universities and NS universities. Answers were organized along a Likert scale ranging from 1 (completely disagree) to 7 (completely agree), so the mean is at 4.

It appears that information about dropout rates, rates of success at exams, and the first salary of the former students (bold) are relatively readily available, but in the case of salaries, less readily available in HSS universities and NS universities than for all institutions. If we now compare HSS and NS, we observe that evaluations by students are still rather rare in France, and rarer in HSS than in

Table 1
Data available about teaching

Questions: is it easy for you to get data about...	HSS university	NS university	All	Number
Drop-out rates	5.38	4.99	**5.24**	1987
Students' evaluations of training programmes?	**2.95**	**3.82**	**3.71**	1907
Number of complementary hours?	**4.23**	**3.76**	**4.01**	1945
Access of students to the job market?	4.23	4.32	4.29	1991
Social origin of your students?	**4.36**	**3.74**	**4.14**	1968
Rates of success at the exams?	5.65	5.24	**5.52**	1994
Average salary at their first position?	3.44	3.73	**5.52**	1973
How many hours each one teaches?	**4.39**	**4.29**	**3.58**	1964

Table 2
Data available about research

Question: is it easy for you to get data about...	HSS university	NS university	All	Number
The number of patents (if relevant in your field)	**2.95**	**4.02**	**3.63**	1176
The number of research grants and their origin	**3.89**	**4.15**	3.96	1867
Expenses and resources for each grant	**3.23**	**3.59**	**3.35**	1830
The number of publications in your unit (department, laboratory, school, etc.)	**4.12**	**4.78**	**4.44**	1907
The quality of these publications	**3.51**	**4.21**	3.83	1885

NS.[10] By contrast, in NS universities, data are less frequent than in HSS universities about complementary hours (maybe because they are not as frequent in the NS because of the decrease in student numbers) and on the social origins of their students.[11] As for the numbers of hours taught by the faculty staff, the figures are about the same in the two kinds of institutions and in both cases higher than for all institutions.

If we then turn to data available about research activities (Table 2), it was quite a surprise to see that on average they are less available than for teaching: the highest score is 4.44 (number of publications in your unit). They furthermore exhibit more differences between the HSS and NS universities. Leaving patents aside, there are statistically significant differences about the number of grants and their origin, the running budgets, the number of publications and their quality. In all cases, the science institutions are better informed (although never reaching the number of 5), especially concerning research grants and the quality of publications.

When looking at the data at hand, it therefore seems that the two groups of institutions do not exactly focus on the same type of data, HSS universities being globally more aware of data on teaching than on research.

The use of indicators

A second group of questions in the survey was concerned with the use of data and looked at four specific types of use: (i) legitimation (or reporting about activities), (ii) evaluation (diagnostic use of data to monitor organizational outcomes and correct deviations from present standards of performance [3], (iii) discussion (interactive use of data in order to learn and interact about them) and (iv) decision

---

[10]Only the cells in bold are statistically significant [ANOVA (analysis of variance) = 0].

[11]In France, academics are supposed to teach 192 hours a year. Because the access to the undergraduate levels is not selective, the number of hours of teaching might be higher than the number of hours academics should teach. Therefore some of them accept more than 192 teaching hours and are paid extra for that: these are the complementary hours.

(using data for change and action). We asked questions about the use of data on teaching, research and budgets. When looking at the results for 'all universities' in the three tables below, the highest scores (closest to 5) show that for teaching (Table 3) and budget (Table 4), the principal use of data is linked to reporting, sometimes to evaluation, but rarely to decision. It is somewhat different in the case of data on research (Table 5) where the main use is concerned with evaluating and where decision is more frequent. It therefore seems that French universities first of all produce data in order to report about their activities and thus look legitimate to those asking for such information. On the other hand, they almost never use data in order to act and make decisions, although one can see that the impact on the allocation of budget is always higher than 4. But more generally, there is still a rather rare use of data to evaluate and compare and make decisions based on such evaluation. But is what is true in general also true for specific categories of universities? Do science-oriented universities make different use of data than the

Table 3
Uses of data on teaching

	Question: data on teaching are used to...	HSS university	NS university	All	Number
Decide	**Decide how to allocate budgets**	**4.45**	**4.10**	4.10	1662
	Rethink teaching programmes	4.11	4.14	4.17	1675
Evaluation	Compare your unit to others	4.36	4.16	4.18	1644
	Set objectives for your unit	3.84	3.71	3.78	1656
	Evaluate the teaching programmes of the university?	4.88	4.92	**4.94**	1722
	Evaluate the quality of your teaching programmes	**3.73**	**4.04**	4.00	1679
	Assess how well your unit is achieving its objectives	4.55	4.60	4.60	1687
Discussion	**Have a common basis for discussion within the university?**	**4.29**	**4.20**	4.18	1664
	Discuss and debate on teaching projects	3.88	3.89	3.91	1665
Legitimation	**Negotiate with schools or departments**	**4.81**	**4.39**	4.44	1637
	Negotiate with the Ministry, the Region or other partners	5.26	5.19	**5.11**	1651
	Do as everybody does, but nobody uses these data	3.35	3.48	3.40	1603
	Document the indicators for the LOLF	5.60	5.58	**5.53**	1645

LOLF, Loi organique relative aux lois de finances/legislation that governs public finance.

Table 4
Uses of data on budget

	Question: data on budget and costs are used to...	HSS university	NS university	All	Number
Decide	Decide how to allocate budgets	4.74	4.69	**4.68**	1675
	Make decisions on investments	4.44	4.37	4.43	1656
	Give you information on your financial situation	4.21	4.24	4.19	1689
	Decide how much to charge for teaching or research activities	3.35	3.86	3.69	1596
Evaluation	Know the costs of the different training programmes	4.73	4.52	4.59	1677
	Know the costs of research activities	4.29	4.37	4.39	1617
	Compare your unit with others	4.55	4.26	4.27	1671
	Assess how your unit is managed	4.69	4.24	4.49	1710
	Assess how the university is managed	4.99	4.75	**4.89**	1746
	Set objectives for your unit	**4.00**	**3.81**	3.92	1689
	Assess whether you achieved these objectives	4.72	4.52	4.57	1697
Discussion	**Have a common basis for discussion within the university**	**4.45**	**4.46**	4.43	1675
	Discuss and debate about priorities	4.10	4.06	4.07	1679
Legitimation	Negotiate budgets with schools and department	4.72	4.63	**4.62**	1674
	Negotiate with the Ministry, the Region or other partners	5.30	5.32	**5.27**	1699
	Document the indicators for the LOLF	5.60	5.48	**5.45**	1676

LOLF, Loi organique relative aux lois de finances/legislation that governs public finance.

humanities- and the social science-oriented universities? Again, only the statistically significant differences (ANOVA = 0) between the two groups will be taken into account.

Looking first at data on teaching (Table 3), even if some results are significantly different, they do not reveal clear-cut discrepancies between HSS and NS universities. We can only note that the use of data on teaching to allocate budgets

Table 5
Uses of data on research

	Question: data on research are used to...	HSS university	NS university	All	Number
Decide	Decide how to allocate budgets	4.76	4.89	**4.74**	1608
	Decide about research priorities	**4.13**	**4.37**	4.27	1610
	Make decisions on investments	**3.98**	**4.26**	4.15	1546
Evaluation	**Compare your unit with others**	**4.70**	**5.18**	**4.83**	1612
	Evaluate the research activities of the faculty staff	5.17	5.33	**5.26**	1654
	Evaluate the research activities of your unit	**5.46**	**5.76**	**5.58**	1638
	Evaluate the research activities of the university	**5.56**	**5.88**	**5.68**	1683
	Set objectives for your unit	3.86	3.97	3.94	1604
	Assess whether you achieved your objectives	4.64	4.53	4.57	1605
Discussion	**Have common basis for discussion within the university**	**4.37**	**4.57**	4.38	1605
	Discuss and debate about research priorities	**4.11**	**4.29**	4.19	1621
Legitimation	Negotiate with schools or departments	4.29	4.34	4.25	1565
	Negotiate with the Ministry, Region, partners	5.24	5.36	**5.27**	1609
	Do as everybody does, but nobody uses these data	3.07	2.78	2.87	1496
	Document the indicators for the LOLF	5.62	5.62	**5.53**	1547

LOLF, Loi organique relative aux lois de finances/legislation that governs public finance.

is somewhat higher in HSS than in NS and that HSS also use these data more to negotiate within the university. The same holds true for data on budget. Very few items are significantly different, and when the differences are significant, they are not striking.

The comparison between the two groups of universities is more interesting and revealing when data for research are concerned (Table 5). On all items for which the differences are statistically significant, the results for science-oriented institutions are higher than the HSS universities. They are therefore more able to decide about research priorities, to make decisions on investments, to compare their unit with others, to evaluate their research activities (at the level of their unit and for the university), to have a common basis for discussions within the university and finally to discuss and to debate about research priorities. This confirms what we observed in the interviews and must be connected to the scientists' rather positive attitudes vis-à-vis indicators, compared with the faculty staff in HSS.

Conclusion

Producing and collecting data has become more and more usual in France after the reforms of the 1990s and 2000s, and there is a clear development towards internal auditing and performance measures in French universities. Although the acceptance of this trend seems easier in science-oriented institutions than in HSS-oriented institutions, the attitude towards indicators is also linked to how they were set and whether they were negotiated or imposed.

    We also observed that the use of the data does not differ substantially between the two groups of universities, especially in the case of data on teaching and budget that are mostly used in these institutions as in all other French institutions first of all for reporting, and thus legitimizing what is done. For data on research there are clearer trends: NS institutions have more information about their research activity than HSS institutions and are more able than the latter to use them to promote evaluation and decision-making.

    The above conclusions are probably transitory because the development of performance measures and the use of indicators are still rather new phenomena, but they nevertheless reveal a rather important change in French universities. This is especially true for research, where the central role played by the ANR and the AERES in producing evaluation and providing norms about what research should be [15] legitimizes the attention paid to research indicators by the university managers and by the directors of the research units.

References

1.   Pontille, D. and Torny, D. (2013) La manufacture de l'évaluation scientifique: algorithmes, jeux de données, outils bibliométriques. *Réseaux* **31**, 25–61
2.   Karpik, L. (2011) What is the price of a scientific paper? In *The Worth of Goods: Valuation and Pricing in the Economy* (Beckert, J. and Aspers, P., eds), pp. 63–85, Oxford University Press, Oxford
3.   Simons, R. (1995) *Levers of Control*. Harvard University Press, Cambridge
4.   Cavalluzzo, K.S. and Ittner, C.D. (2004) Implementing performance management innovations: evidence from government. *Accounting, Organizations and Society* **29**, 243–267
5.   Musselin, C. (2001) *La Longue Marche des Universités Françaises*. PUF, Paris. Also available as: (2004) *The Long March of French Universities*. Routledge, New York
6.   Charle, C. (1994) *La République des Universitaires*. Seuil, Paris
7.   de Boer, H., Enders, J. and Leisyte, L. (2007) On striking the right notes: shifts in governance and the organizational transformation of universities. *Public Administration* **85**, 27–46
8.   Krücken, G. and Meier, F. (2006) Turning the university into and organizational actor. In *Globalization and Organization: World Society and Organizational Change* (Drori, G., Meyer, J. and Hwang, H., eds), pp. 241–257, Oxford University Press, Oxford
9.   Musselin, C. (2006) Are universities specific organisations? In *Towards a Multiversity? Universities Between Global Trends and National Traditions* (Krücken, G., KosMützky, A. and Torka, M., eds), pp. 63–84, Transcript Verlag, Bielefeld
10. Whitley, R. (2008) Universities as strategic actors: limitations and variations. In *The University in the Market* (Engwall, L. and Weaire, D., eds), pp. 23–37, Portland Press, London

11. Power, M. (1997) *The Audit Society: Rituals of Verification*. Oxford University Press, Oxford

12. Chatelain-Ponroy, S. and Sponem, S. (2007) Les pratiques des établissements d'enseignement supérieur et de recherche en matière de pilotage et de contrôle de gestion. *Revue Française de Comptabilité* **401**, 41–45

13. Musselin, C. (2012) *Liberté, Responsabilité… et Centralisation des Universités*. Monograph, Centre de Sociologie des Organisations, Paris. http://cso.edu/upload/dossiers/Rapport_Liber teResponsabiliteCentralisationUniversites_2012.pdf

14. Chatelain-Ponroy, S., Mignot-Gérard, S., Musselin, C. and Sponem, S. (2012) *La Gouvernance des Universités. Pouvoir, Evaluation et Identité*. Monograph, Centre de Sociologie des Organisations, Paris. http://cso.edu/upload/dossiers/Rapport_GouvernanceUniversitesFrance_ 2012.pdf

15. Musselin, C. (2013) How peer review empowers the academic profession and university managers: changes in relationships between the state, universities and the professoriate. *Research Policy* **42**, 1165–1173

PART VI: CONCLUSIONS

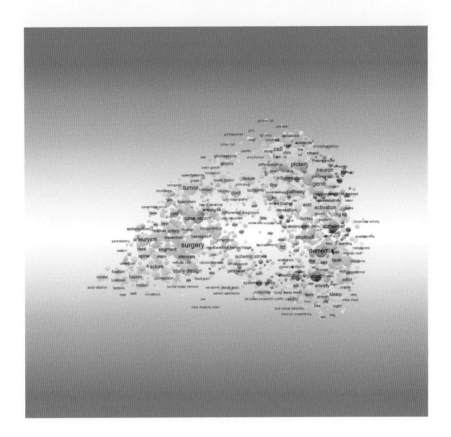

14 **Science as big business**
Wim Blockmans, Lars Engwall and Denis Weaire

PART VI: CONCLUSION

Science as big business

Wim Blockmans*[1], Lars Engwall†[2] and Denis Weaire‡[3]
*Institute for History, Leiden University, The Netherlands, †Department of Business Studies, Uppsala University, Sweden, and ‡Institute of Physics, Trinity College Dublin, Ireland

The expansion of the system

Over the last decades, new forms of evaluation and the intensity of their application have gradually taken such proportions that the whole character of the scholarly world is now infected by a kind of scientometric mania. Modern information technologies, the strong expansion in the number of researchers and their number of publications have generated new requirements for the management of evaluations and new tools to accomplish it [1]. Moreover, easier transportation facilities have considerably increased scholars' mobility on a global scale, which has accelerated and intensified their contacts. The budgets involved in the increasingly expensive material and personnel of laboratories have required closer scrutiny of the results of the huge investments, especially where most of them were made with public money, as prevails in Europe. This is indeed demonstrated by Nicola Gulley, who in Chapter 8 quotes an average annual growth of 3% in researchers and articles since the late 1940s in the STM (science, technology and medicine) fields. The accelerating tempo of research output is further illustrated by the 200-fold increase from 1985 to 2012 in the number of papers submitted to *Angewandte Chemie*, mainly due to the massive contribution of non-German researchers. The evaluation process, including desk assessment, thousands of referee reports and a redress procedure, leads to a very high refusal rate, which can be seen as the price that needs to be paid for top quality. More generally, Gulley quotes a 44% increase in the published papers in her field over the years 2000–2010.

Garfield's innovation

The huge expansion of the research area had implications for the organization of the critical assessment of the results, as well as for the overall management of the profession and the significant financial flows it absorbs. Responding to the first challenge, a radically new approach was presented in 1955 by Dr Eugene K. Garfield in his seminal article 'Citation Indexes for Science: A New Dimension in Documentation through Association of Ideas' [2]. He claimed that "the Citation Index bypasses some of the limitations of classical subject indexing" ([3], p. 650), and, according to Yancey [4], he envisioned information tools that allow

[1]Email: wimblockmans7@gmail.com
[2]Email: lars.engwall@fek.uu.se
[3]Email: dweaire@tcd.ie

researchers to expedite their research process, evaluate the impact of their work, spot scientific trends and trace the history of modern scientific thoughts. Garfield realized that, since scientific indexes were discipline-oriented, researchers weren't finding all of the information relevant to their work. Researching a scientific area solely by its subject or keywords limited findings by ignoring relevant papers from other disciplines. By indexing scholarly work by citation, he allowed researchers to track what other works a paper has referenced, and how many times others have cited a paper. And by counting citations, the 'impact factor' could be measured, *assigning an indicator of quality* [Authors' italics] to more influential works.

Garfield founded the Institute for Scientific Information in Philadelphia which, at the moment when it was acquired by the Thomson Corporation in 1992, employed 500 people. It collected cited references found in 8700 of the world's leading scholarly science and technical journals covering more than 100 disciplines and going back to 1900. However, he stated himself that "a citation index must meet the same economic test that all products in our society must meet: does the cost justify the benefits?" [3]. Although his method demonstrated the central role played by a few journals in the natural sciences, he acknowledged that the fields of the humanities and most of the social sciences operate in a different way, which made its application to these domains economically not feasible. After all, he worked with a commercial company.

Although initially Garfield had in mind to facilitate bibliographic searches beyond disciplinary boundaries, increasingly his citation index was used primarily as a measure of the impact of an article, a researcher, a group, an institute, a journal, a discipline or even the research performance of a whole country. And increasingly, the simple and assumedly objective figure was assigned the role of a proxy for *an indicator of quality*, which would facilitate all kinds of evaluations. As Giuseppe Longo and several other authors in this volume argue, numbers replaced value and, to paraphrase Richard R. Ernst [5], reading was replaced by counting. Popularity of a topic within a time span of just a few years is not automatically an indication of innovative and significant research. Or, as Jane Grimson formulates it in her chapter:

> "*traditional bibliometrics* [...] *define what constitutes research quality rather than providing objective measures of research quality.* [...] [They] *measure, however imperfectly, only some of the dimensions of research quality, and there is no substitute for a detailed study of the researcher's output.*"

Garfield himself saw the limitations of his metrics and tried to address them by ever more complicated calculations. Thus he checked the citation frequency of Nobel Prize winners, but it remained too labour-intensive to isolate the references to publications *before* the award for all the laureates. He observed that a "high level of citation will fail to detect, for example, publications from small, specialty fields", also in the domains of physics, chemistry, and physiology and medicine ([6], p. 183). He defined a 'Citation Classic' as a paper receiving more than 300 citations, but admitted that "only the rarest paper is cited more than 300 times within a few years of publication". And, even if "most citations to a paper [in these three scientific domains] are received in the first decade after publication", the phenomenon of delayed recognition occurs. He discussed, for example, the case of A.M. Cormack who was awarded the Nobel Prize for Medicine in 1979 for articles published in the specialized *Journal of Applied Physics* in 1963 and 1964. These had been virtually ignored until G.N. Hounsfield recognized in them the mathematical foundations for the CAT scanner and scored more than 800 citations with his paper. Cormack's invention had been obliterated by incorporation in another paper. And Garfield concluded: "Only peer judgement can determine which of these authors is uniquely qualified for the Nobel or some other illustrious award. Indeed, citation frequency by itself is not adequately indicative of outstanding and influential publications" ([6], p. 186).

The impact of Garfield

The citation index was nevertheless welcomed by administrators and scholars as a timesaving tool for all kinds of evaluations, which had become an increasingly heavy burden for senior scholars. Applicants to the European Union FP7 (Seventh Framework Programme) have been encouraged to mention the Thomson Reuters impact factor of their publications, and many research councils and universities apply this instrument in their selection procedures. In Chapters 5 and 9, Michel Gevers and Jan Reedijk respectively produce clear examples of the ways by which some commercial publishers seek to steer authors towards reinforcement of the 'impact' of their own journals.

As recounted by Milena Žic Fuchs in Chapter 11, a reaction came from the American Society for Cell Biology, which formulated on the 16 December 2012 DORA, a Declaration on Research Assessment. It has been subscribed by hundreds of scientific institutions and organizations, including the Academia Europaea. Its first recommendation reads as follows [7]:

> *"Do not use journal-based metrics, such as journal impact factors, as a surrogate measure of the quality of individual research articles, to assess an individual scientist's contributions, or in hiring, promotion or funding decisions."*

This very welcome warning concerns just one of the various indicators which have been applied without the required prudence for some time. Self-evidently, candidates will adapt their publishing behaviour and their applications in function of the prevailing criteria.

By now, a variety of indicators have been developed, but all of them have their limitations, as most authors in the present volume demonstrate. Anthony van Raan, one of the leading initiators of bibliometrics in Europe, whose calculations have been based on the Web of Science and Scopus databases, acknowledges in Chapter 3 that bibliometric performance analyses have to be used as information in combination with peer review. His institute has been developing ever more sophisticated methods such as mapping on the basis of keywords (see his Figure 3 and the book cover), and new indicators, the latest being called the 'crown indicator'. But at the same time, he lists no fewer than 11 weaknesses of the existing tools.

Jane Grimson enumerates the biases by disciplines, dealing with interdisciplinarity, language, region, format of publication, and non-attributable multi-authorship. The trickiest shortcoming remains the short time span of the counting of citations, which makes it very unlikely that truly groundbreaking insights will be fully recognized in the citation indices. "Truly original work takes more than 2 years to be appreciated" [8]. Some book publications, including critical editions of sources in the humanities, remain standard references for a century and more [9].

Problems outside the 'hard' sciences

Despite such objections, these apparently objective and simple instruments were especially convenient for science administrators, who tended to prescribe and use them indiscriminately for all disciplines. By doing so, they may have systematically favoured those disciplines for which the bibliometrics had been designed, and harmed others. Best off were disciplines of which the object is global or even universal, so that all findings are equally relevant for specialists throughout the whole world. Taking the advantage of economies of scale, such disciplines have organized themselves globally, which made the production of widely disseminated journals attractive to international publishers. In turn, it became rewarding and prestigious to publish in such journals, to be invited as a reviewer and to serve as a member of the editorial board. That attraction made it even possible for science journals to require a fee for the publication of an article, which they sell to providers, libraries and users, whereas they did not contribute to the research costs. This self-reinforcing mechanism led to standardization of publications and the establishing of a ranking within large disciplines. North American and British journals became globally dominant. In the wake of this development, we have obtained institutional rankings, which, as pointed out by Michel Gevers, Giovanni Abramo and Linda Wedlin, have a number of shortcomings.

However, as demonstrated in Chapter 13 by Christine Musselin and her co-authors, for a variety of reasons the science model does not fit all disciplines. This is further shown by Milena Žic Fuchs, who discusses data produced by Gunnar Sivertsen demonstrating that Scopus covers hardly more than 10% of the humanities publications and just one-third of those in the social sciences. For the Web of Science, the coverage reaches 16% and 22% respectively [10]. Similar results were obtained at an evaluation at Uppsala University in 2007, when the publications of university researchers were matched with Web of Science. It turned out that Web of Science covered 79.2% of the publications in the area of medicine and pharmacy, 57.0% in the area of science and technology and 8.3% in the area of the humanities and social sciences ([11], pp. 90–91).

Mathematicians, computer scientists, and technical and engineering scientists joined the large majority of the humanities and social scientists in stressing the adequacy of the particular publication methods typical of their disciplines, which do not relate well to the citations system. They address technical, societal and cultural problems for which the most appropriate audience is not necessarily to be found in a global forum and for which the most effective expression is not uniquely a short journal article in a highly formalized type of English, co-signed by numerous authors. Even more devastating is the observation that a blind eye is turned by all too many authors to the vast body of knowledge produced over time in various national languages. In culturally specific domains, this can lead to poorly informed publications in highly reputed international media.

As a consequence, it comes as no surprise that in a number of small European countries, beginning with Norway and followed by Denmark, Finland and Belgium (Flanders), governments have taken initiatives to construct databases of national publications which meet the international standards of peer-reviewed publication. Typically, they include books, collective volumes and articles in the national language. These systems are described and compared in Chapter 12 by Frederik Verleysen, Pol Ghesquière and Tim Engels who demonstrate that different procedures lead to considerable variation in the results. As with the European Reference Index for the humanities discussed by Milena Žic Fuchs, the inclusive databases offer the advantage of covering all the media of peer-reviewed scholarly publications, but lack fine tuning with regard to the status and circulation that journals and publishing houses really have, both within national borders and internationally. Such precise weighting of components is indeed important, since many of the databases have a direct financial impact. For instance, as the Flemish database is applied, it accounts for 6.28% of the budget distributed by the government to universities. It has been revised over the last years, and even now one may wonder if the proportion of 4 to 1 applied to the weight of a monograph (for example, a published PhD thesis) compared with a journal article, is fair or still detrimental to the book-publishing disciplines.

Problems in the assessments

All of these endeavours, contested by many serious researchers, are costly, time-consuming and bureaucratic. For instance, the 2008 Research Assessment Exercise is estimated to have cost the U.K. government approximately £60 million; £12 million to perform it and an additional £47 million for the universities to prepare the submissions [12]. The outcomes of this have been widely publicized and discussed publicly. Major newspapers published rankings and commented on shifts in comparison with the 2001 exercise. All of this enhanced a spirit of competition at all levels of the higher education system, which was not unequivocally healthy. Staff members are encouraged to aim for a high output of publications; other duties may be less valued and consequently neglected. Top journals have to keep their subscribers, so they have to cultivate reputations as guarantors of high-quality research. It is acknowledged, as also pointed out by Lars Engwall, that reviewers tend to give conservative assessments, which discourages risk-taking proposals. A recent analysis addressing three types of assessment, the subjective reviews after publication, the journal impact factor and the citations, observed the absence of correlation between the assessors. Experts showed to be prejudiced by the journal impact factor. But also the impact factor is 'extremely error prone' and the citations 'inherently highly stochastic' [13,14].

Even if errors cannot be entirely excluded by peer review, that procedure offers far better guarantees than the mushrooming online open-access journals which have far less transparent structures and procedures than established printed journals. Online journals are not bound by limits in page space and are eager to publish in return for a fee. *Science* published in its 4 October 2013 special issue on 'Communication in Science: Pressures and Predators' the results of a fake research article submitted to 305 online open-access journals. It was rejected by 98, but accepted by 157 of them, mainly based in India, in return for a fee of $3100. The sheer volume of online publications these days makes it harder to distinguish between respectable and questionable journals [15].

Besides the perceived facilitation of review procedures, bibliometrics has been espoused by science managers seeking primarily quantitative, allegedly objective instruments for the distribution of resources and the control of the performance. In the context of the considerable growth of public spending for research, it is certainly justified to hold scientists accountable. However, as the progress of science is inherently not straightforward or predictable, the research community feels itself uncomfortable with over-simplified, 'auditable' measurements of immediate outcomes, especially as they impose a substantial extra workload and are considered to be speciously precise. The researchers' real target being discovery and innovation, they feel that the heavy burden of research evaluations is expensive and inadequate, leading to compliant attitudes, risk avoidance, cynicism and even unethical behaviour (see Chapter 10 and [16,17]). In general, bibliometric devices do not provide proper means to account for the societal mission that science also has to fulfil. The U.K. Research Evaluation, re christened the REF (Research Excellence Framework), will include this function as a criterion, weighted by 20% in 2014 [18]. Which implies that all previous exercises have been biased in this respect?

> "*The REF will for the first time explicitly assess the impact of research beyond academia, as well as assessing the academic excellence of research. One purpose of the REF is to reward research departments in universities that engage with business, the public sector and civil society organizations, and carry new ideas through to beneficial outcomes [...] Impact is defined as: any effect on, change or benefit to the economy, society, culture, public policy or services, health, the environment or quality of life, beyond academia.*"

New discussions will arise, and they have effectively started already, about the methods to be used to assess "the impact of research beyond academia" [19]. This appears from the conclusions of a prospective study published in November 2013 by the Royal Netherlands Academy of Sciences to advise the government about the 'public investment in knowledge and the value of research' ([20], pp. 11,13).

> "*It is essential to understand that the effect of research policy can only be usefully evaluated in the long term; that is where the effect is felt.*
>
> *There are plenty of empirical studies available that link public and private expenditure on R&D to GDP growth at the macro-economic level. These provide sufficient evidence that the economic value of research can be*

measured and analysed. It is understandable that the elasticities found in these studies vary; this is, to some extent, the result of spill-overs, serendipity, and variations in policy and in the broader innovation system.

Quantitative studies exploring the value of research do not make allowance for much of the broader economic and social value of research because that value is difficult to quantify, especially in the short term. The value of research is not limited to its present or future contribution to GDP, and only part of that value lies in its productivity effects. It is much more difficult to measure the overall economic and social value of research."

Of course, in calling into question recent developments, we have been dealing in generalizations. We should admit that there are honourable exceptions. In particular, the European Research Council, in its relentless pursuit of *excellence*, clearly a subjective concept, has so far resisted putting bibliometrics in the forefront of its evaluations. Rather, it relies primarily on the judgment of expert panels. For the Starting and Consolidators' Grants, panels meet face-to-face with the short-listed candidates, and then debate their merits across the table. It is a time-consuming process that some would call old-fashioned, but in a few years it has won admiration and respect.

Recommendations

To conclude, we venture to formulate some general recommendations which result from the papers in this volume.

1. Rich multidimensional assessment tools are needed to recognize and value the different contributions made by individuals, regardless of their discipline.
2. Evaluations, especially those on the individual level, should not be based on metrics only. They should be used only in combination with other factors, and taking into account their limitations.
3. It should be recognized that different factors are important to different people and depend on the research context, which calls into question any reliance on rigid weightings.
4. Criteria need to be adequate to the field, its size, standards and societal role.
5. Qualitative evaluations by experts, informed by quantitative indicators, remain the best possible method, addressing issues of scope, originality and value.
6. The journal impact factor should be dismissed, as is proposed in DORA.
7. In the case of multi-author papers, the contributions of individual authors are not distinguishable under current bibliometric systems; for the purposes of evaluation this is a very serious deficiency.
8. Metric indicators should be used for evaluation only to the extent that their inherent biases are well understood by those applying them.

9. Expert reviewers should be adequately recognized and rewarded.

10. The academic community has been overtaken by events: it should make greater efforts to anticipate and influence future developments.

References

1. Drori, G.S., Meyer, J.W., Ramirez, F.O. and Schofer, E. (2003) *Science in the Modern World Polity: Institutionalization and Globalization.* Stanford University Press, Palo Alto

2. Garfield, E. (1955) Citation indexes for science: a new dimension in documentation through association of ideas. *Science* **122**, 108–111. Also available at: http://garfield.library.upenn.edu/papers/science_v122v3159p108y1955.html

3. Garfield, E. (1964) Science citation index. A new dimension in indexing. *Science* **144**, 649–654 [Reprinted in (1984) *Essays of an Information Scientist* 7, pp. 525–535, quote on 526]

4. Yancey, R. (2005) Fifty years of citation indexing and analysis. http://wokinfo.com/essays/50-years-citation-indexing/ (Accessed 21 November 2013)

5. Ernst, R.R. (2010) The follies of citation indices and academic ranking lists. A brief commentary to 'Bibliometrics as weapons of mass citation'. *CHIMIA* **64**, 90

6. Garfield, E. (1986) Do Nobel prize winners write citation classics? *Current Comments* **23**, 3–8 (Reprinted in *Essays of an Information Scientist* 9, 182–187)

7. San Francisco Declaration on Research Assessment. http://www.ascb.org/SFdeclaration.html

8. Lawrence, P.A. (2007) The mismeasurement of science. *Current Biology* **17**, R583–R585

9. Nederhof, A.J. (2006) Bibliometric monitoring of research performance in the social sciences and humanities: a review. *Scientometrics* **66**, 81–100

10. Sivertsen, G. (2011) Achieving complete and comparable data and output indicators for scholarly publishing in the humanities and social sciences. http://bibliometrie.univie.ac.at/fileadmin/user_upload/ub_bibliometrie/sivertsen.pdf (Accessed 22 November 2013)

11. KoF07. Quality and Renewal 2007. An Overall Evaluation of Research at Uppsala University, Uppsala. Uppsala University

12. RAE manager (2009) RAE Manager's report. http://www.rae.ac.uk/pubs/2009/manager/manager.pdf; PA Consulting Group (2008) RAE 2008 Accountability Review. http://www.hefce.ac.uk/media/hefce/content/pubs/2009/rd0809/rd08_09.pdf

13. Eyre-Walker, A. and Stoletzki, N. (2013) The assessment of science: the relative merits of post-publication review, the impact factor, and the number of citations. *PLoS Biology* **11**, e1001675

14. Eisen, J.A., MacCallum, C.J. and Neylon, C. (2013) Expert failure: re-evaluating research assessment. *PLoS Biology* **11**, e1001677

15. Bohannon, J. (2013) Who's afraid of peer review? In *Science*. 4 October 2013, http://www.sciencemag.org/content/342/6154/60.full

16. Power, M. (1997) *The Audit Society: Rituals of Verification.* Oxford University Press, Oxford

17. Sheikh, A. (2000) Publication ethics and the research assessment exercise: reflections on the troubled question of authorship. *Journal of Medical Ethics* **26**, 422–426

18. http://www.ref.ac.uk/panels/assessmentcriteriaandleveldefinitions/; http://www.ref.ac.uk/media/ref/content/researchusers/REF%20guide.pdf

19. Magrs, P. (2013) Re: your REF impact request. In The Times Education. 25 April 2013, http://www.timeshighereducation.co.uk/features/re-your-ref-impact-request/2003342.article; http://blogs.lse.ac.uk/impactofsocialsciences/2013/05/07/absence-of-impact-used-to-be-the-fashionable-thing-to-claim/

20. Public investment in knowledge and the value of research. https://www.knaw.nl/nl/actueel/publicaties/publieke-kennisinvesteringen-en-de-waarde-van-wetenschap

Index